The Romance of Physics

The Romance of Physics

BY KEITH GORDON IRWIN

Illustrated by Anthony Ravielli

Charles Scribner's Sons / NEW YORK

Contents

Introduction

In the language of the ancient Greeks, the word *physics* meant "knowledge of nature." To the Greeks, nature was the world about them. It included all living things—the beasts of the fields, the fowls of the air, the fish of the seas, the insects, and all forms of plant life. The rocks of the hills and the waters of the streams were a part of this knowledge, too. So were the nymphs, satyrs, dryads, gods, and goddesses that this imaginative people thought produced the happy noises of the trees and streams or the angry screams of storms and boisterous seas.

Today, the science of physics deals only with the study of inanimate matter. The portion relating to living things is a part of the science of biology. The gods and goddesses of the ancient world are studied as mythology. But there is still a large field of nature remaining to be assigned to physics: the world of solids, liquids, and gases and the forms of energy related to them—heat, light, electrical energy, mechanical energy, and nuclear energy. Physicists also study the forces of nature, such as gravitation and electrical attraction and repulsion.

Nature can be observed, but it is not a teacher or a consultant. "Nature," we say, "will there be rain on Saturday?" There is no response. "Nature, why is the rainbow so perfectly round, and where do the colors go when it fades away?" There is still no reply. "Nature, why does a film of oil calm the tempestuous waves?" "Nature, have all the great discoveries been made, or are there still some left?" Again, no answer. We say that things behave according to certain laws of nature, and we are right. But it is man, not nature, who records these laws. All of physics is a man-made science in which the laws of nature that have been found and tested are phrased in the words of men. The theories of physics are man-made, too. Their purpose is to explain logically the phenomena of nature; these ideas require imagination.

Man's knowledge of the various forces and phenomena of nature has often been slow and irregular in developing. In some centuries, however, a number of men caught glimpses of great new things. Because of *their* work, for a time progress was rapid. *The Romance of Physics* is their story.

PART I / *Three Great Pioneers*

Of the various forces of nature studied in physics, the first to be examined adequately was *gravitation*, which is the force of attraction between two bodies. The weight of an object on the earth is determined by the earth's gravitational pull on it. We rarely think of this force as a strange one—but it is.

Gravitation cannot be shifted to new positions. It cannot be cut off in any way. No object can be hidden anywhere beyond its reach. No moving body can race so fast as to escape its pull. Not a single atom, for all its inconceivable tininess, can escape the pull of gravitation, and across the almost limitless distances of space, that same force holds the celestial bodies in orbit.

This strange force, and the histories of three great pioneers—Archimedes, Galileo Galilei, and Isaac Newton—who made great contributions to our understanding of it, forms the first part of the story of physics.

Archimedes

CHAPTER 1

Archimedes:
Mathematician and Inventor

Archimedes lived twenty-two centuries ago in the ancient sea-port city of Syracuse, on the eastern side of the island of Sicily, in the Mediterranean Sea. He died in the year 212 B.C., at the age of seventy-five. He was of Greek ancestry and spoke the Greek language with the accent peculiar to the people of Syracuse. His father, Phidias, was an astronomer, perhaps a teacher as well.

The Joyous Mathematician of Syracuse

About the boyhood days of Archimedes we know nothing. He might have made models of boats, doing it with accuracy and care. It would not be a surprising hobby for a boy of Syracuse, for the city was noted for its well-protected harbor, and ships were an important part of its life. Fast patrol boats, with tiers of rowers, guarded the harbor and nearby shores. Large cargo vessels out of Egypt or Phoenicia, at the eastern end of the Mediterranean, stopped in the harbor to load or unload the products of trade. Arriving more frequently were smaller boats with gaily colored sails that had their trade routes in the western Mediterranean. There were also the little fishing boats that left the harbor in the morning, to return as the sun went down. It was models of ships like these that the boy probably whittled from wood, polishing them with lumps of finely grained stone moistened with olive oil.

The first recorded event in the life story of Archimedes came in his young manhood. The details are vague, but Phidias had apparently made plans to go to Alexandria, in Egypt, for a few months and told his son he could accompany him if he wished. Alexandria was a Mediterranean seaport near the mouth of the Nile River. It had been founded a century before by Alexander the Great. The language spoken was Greek, and a famous Greek school was located there. Phidias had some problems in astronomy to talk over with the schoolmen of Alexandria, and Archimedes probably went joyously along.

We must even do some guessing about the length of that stay in Egypt. It would at the least have lasted from the late autumn of one year to the early spring of the next, since the sailing vessels traversing the waters of the Mediterranean avoided the storms of winter. As for Archimedes' experiences in Egypt, he seems to have visited the Pyramids. He would certainly have watched men raising the Nile water in buckets for irrigation and have examined the working models of engineering projects in Alexandria. We also know that he met the schoolmen of Alexandria. Apparently he sat in on their discussions of the study of the branch of mathematics we call *geometry*, which in his time would have been known as the *Elements of Euclid.*

Euclid was a great Greek scholar who had taught in Alexandria about fifty years before. He had gathered and sorted out all of the propositions then known about the geometry of lines, angles, and simple curves. His findings were presented in the thirteen books of his *Elements.* Since printing had not been developed, anyone desiring his own copy of even a portion of the whole would have had to copy it by hand or hire someone to do it. Euclid had kept no record of where he had found his original materials. His contribution had been to edit these materials so as to bring out the logical step-by-step argument that formed the proof of each proposition. The school at Alexandria had doubtless many copies of Euclid's *Elements* and added more propositions to those given as they were developed. But no new proposition was accepted that did not give with exactness an argument that followed that of Euclid. No other proof would be necessary or allowed.

Archimedes was familiar with Euclid's *Elements.* They were probably a part of his father's library. He must have wondered whether all of the propositions of geometry had already been worked out or whether there were some as yet undiscovered. Years later, when he was a man, Archimedes proved several new propositions as part of the immense amount of mathematical work he undertook, and he sent the proofs to the schoolmen of Alexandria. Archimedes' mathematical activities were famous, and his neighbors called him "the joyous mathematician of Syracuse."

The Problem of the King's Crown

Everyone in Syracuse from King Hiero to the men at the wharf knew that Archimedes was fond of mathematical problems. One day the king had a problem for him to work, one that has gone down in history. After saving the required gold for several years, Hiero had arranged to have a new crown made. His goldworkers were very skillful in preparing the crown according to exact specifications as to its size and weight. But the King, who seems to have been quite suspicious, felt that he had been cheated—that some silver had been used and then covered with gold, even though the total weight checked perfectly with the figures he had given.

Hiero knew that he could melt the crown to see if it was made of both gold and silver, or he could drill small holes in it and test the metal brought out by the drill. But these procedures would spoil the beauty of his crown.

Finally, he thought of seeking the assistance of Archimedes. The great mathematician probably knew nothing about work with precious metals, but he might have an idea as to how the problem could be solved without damaging the crown.

Upon talking to Hiero, Archimedes seems to have had one idea immediately. Gold is over 19 times as heavy as water; silver is much lighter than gold. Equal weights of gold and silver would have different volumes. If he knew the *volume* of the crown and the space it occupied, he could solve the problem almost instantly. He knew the weight of, let us say, a cubic inch of water, and a cubic inch of gold would weigh more than 19 times as much. Using the measurement of the crown's volume, if he had it, he could calculate what the crown should weigh if it was pure gold. However, the volume would be hard to get, for the crown's shape was irregular and could not be found mathematically.

Archimedes told the King that he would think about the problem. He was still considering it when he went to the public bath. Then, as his body sank into the water, an idea came to him. When an object sinks, it pushes the water out of the way as it goes down. The volume of the water pushed aside would surely be the same as the body's own volume. Leaping excitedly from the bath, Archimedes went racing toward his workshop, shouting joyously as he ran, "Eureka! Eureka! I have found it!" As he ran, he may have thought what he would do when he got to his workshop. He would want a tank large enough to hold the crown. The tank, filled to the brim with water, would need an overflow spout to catch any liquid being displaced as the crown was submerged. Some vessel would have to be set under the tip of the spout to catch the water so it could be weighed. When its weight was multiplied by 19, would the figure be the same as the crown's weight? If so, the gold was pure. Or would it be less? If this was the case, there was silver in the crown, or it was hollow.

Two different endings have been recorded by the storytellers of ancient times, so you may take your choice. In one version

the jeweler tried to cheat the King and was beheaded. In the other the jeweler was exonerated.

Boats That Float and Boats That Sink

Archimedes probably continued experimenting with a tank like the one he had prepared for the crown problem; perhaps he started by using the old wooden boat models he had made as a boy. From that he went on to see for the first time why some boats capsize or sink and others float.

The details of his experiments have not been preserved, only his mathematical proofs and his conclusions. But we can imagine that we are in Archimedes' workshop, looking over his shoulder as he and his assistant experiment. Let us suppose that some boat models are being "put to sea" in the tank, one at a time. Each has been weighed, then placed in the full tank, and the water that overflowed has been kept in a container. The water's weight is recorded, and Archimedes reaches the same conclusion by testing boat after boat: The weight of a body that floats in water with its top at the water's surface is the same as the weight of an equal volume of water. If the body weighs less than an equal volume of water, it will displace only an amount of water equal to its own weight, and float higher. When the weight of the water that overflows is less than the weight of the body, it will sink. The arrangement in the tank can be modified so that the boat model that sinks is suspended below one pan of a balance, and it can be weighed either in the air or when submerged in water.

After several trials, Archimedes had reached this conclusion: If a solid heavier than water is weighed in water, the weight will

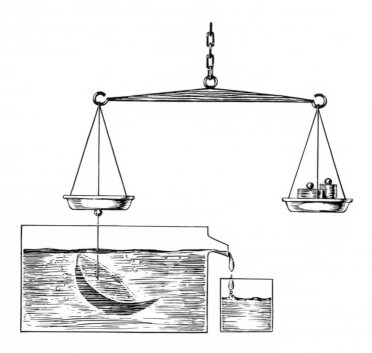

be lighter than its true weight in air by the weight of the liquid displaced.

The last of these conclusions is called the *Principle of Archimedes* and is known to hold true for other liquids besides water as well as for gases in which a body is submerged. The other conclusions, combined, form what are sometimes called the *Laws of Flotation.*

"Nature Is a Mathematician"

Archimedes sent a full description of his findings to the schoolmen of Alexandria, who had many copies of the report made. They were excited by the results, for they showed that nature was a skilled mathematician. They were equally excited by the later reports that Archimedes sent.

One of these was on the *Law of the Lever.* Archimedes' words are now lost, although his ideas are in every physics book. He may have made models of the various weight-lifting devices in use at the time and then studied them in his workshop. The drawings (page 20) indicate the three most important models of *levers,* which are rigid bodies free to rotate around an axis. The illustrations show the weight to be moved, the fulcrum (the triangle), and the effort (the hand). The arrows show the direction in which the effort is applied.

Let us consider a lever with arms of equal length, a fulcrum exactly in the center, and with equal forces acting on each arm. A seesaw is such a lever. The force acting on each arm tends to make the beam rotate around the fulcrum. One force tends to produce clockwise motion and the other counterclockwise rotation. Since these opposing forces are equal in their action, there is no rotation in either direction and the lever is balanced, or in equilibrium. But if one of the forces was larger than the other, or closer to the fulcrum, the lever would begin to turn. The *Law of Moments* states that when a body is in *equilibrium,*

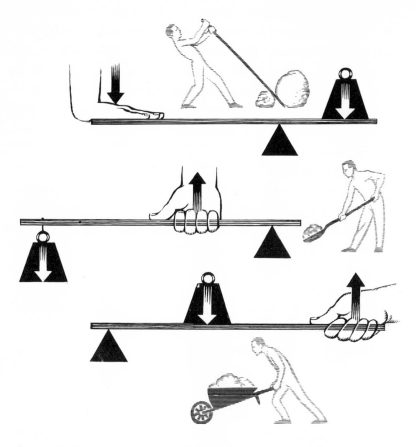

the sum of the clockwise moments (the turning effects of a force) is equal to the sum of the counterclockwise moments.

Archimedes probably noticed also that with a lever there is one point at which it can be balanced on the fulcrum, and only one point. The beam acts as if all its weight were concentrated at this one place, which is called the *center of gravity*.

The Problem of the Tipped Boat

Looking back across the centuries, it is not easy to put the scientific achievements of this great man in the order of their occurrence. At times the sole clue comes from the reports listed by the schoolmen of Alexandria and duplicated by them. Following the report on the lever comes a geometrical treatment of how to determine the center of weight of a *paraboloid of revolution.* This figure is formed by rotating a parabola about its axis. In his study Archimedes found an answer to why a well-balanced boat, after being tipped sideways, will right itself when released, and why a boat may tip over if its mast and sail are too heavy.

Now, a parabola is a kind of a flat curve that can be made by cutting a cone while holding the knife blade exactly parallel to the side of the cone. As the pieces of the cone fall apart, each face will carry on it a perfect parabola. The parabola is not

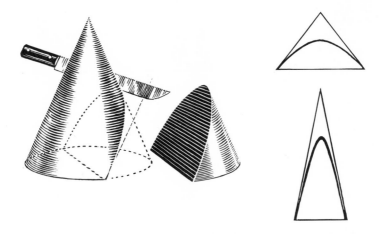

like a circle, which has only one shape for a given diameter; it is a "family" of curves of the same general shape. The parabola formed by cutting the cone depends upon the cone's dimensions. A long, slender one will give an elongated parabola; a chunky one will produce a curve with a wide opening.

When a wooden paraboloid is floated on water, it looks much like a boat without mast and sail: its *center of gravity* is located below the level of the surrounding water. When the

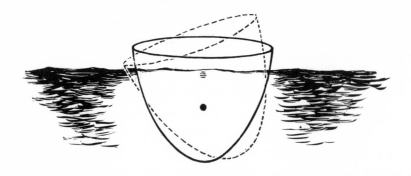

paraboloid is tipped sideways by the hand and then released, it returns to its first position. As the wooden object is tipped, the center of weight is lifted nearer to the water level. When it is released, the center of weight goes down again, taking the lowest possible position. A simplified statement of Archimedes' conclusions would be somewhat as follows: For a floating boat to be stable and not capsize, its center of weight must be below the water level at all times. It is raised when a force tips the boat sideways. If this action does not carry the center of weight higher than the water level, the boat will right itself when the force is released.

The addition of a mast and sail raises the center of weight of a boat as a whole. If its resulting location is above the water level, the boat will capsize.

The Inventions of Archimedes

In addition to Archimedes' fame as a mathematician and scientist, he is also noted for his inventions. About these, no records were transmitted to Alexandria, so there is more uncertainty about the details of the inventions than about his mathematical and scientific accomplishments. Five devices in particular have been credited to him by later writers; one, the lever, has already been discussed. The other four were designed to produce powerful pulls upon ropes and cables. Since no way was then known by which to measure any force but that of weight, the simple mathematical relations between the force exerted and the load moved of these four devices went undetected. All four required, in their construction, parts formed from bronze, so that advances in mining and smelting contributed to the development of these weight-moving devices.

The earliest of the five inventions was a water-raising device for the Nile that must have been produced while Archimedes was in Egypt. It can be called a *spiral pump*, but, unlike modern pumps, it had no pistons or valves, and operated with complete quiet except for the slight gurgle of water running steadily into a trough. As can be seen in the drawing, it consisted of a spiral, or *helix*, of metal tubing wound about a metal axis and

turned by a crank handle. The device was set at an angle, the bottom opening of the helix being under the water's surface, the top opening set over a trough. As the crank handle was turned, the water rose steadily through the coils and poured from the upper opening. It has been used in Egypt ever since Archimedes introduced it. Only one other use in ancient days seems to have been recorded. In Syracuse, legend tells us, Archimedes made one of these pumps quickly to remove the water that had flooded the hull of a large vessel caught in a violent gale.

Another device, pictured here, that Archimedes may have invented was a wheel-and-drum arrangement, now called a *wheel and axle*—a name given it by Isaac Newton. As the illustration shows, the wheel, roughened for better holding, was turned by hand. The drum turned with the wheel and so drew upon the rope that was wrapped around the drum. With this device the power of one man at the wheel gave a pull to the rope

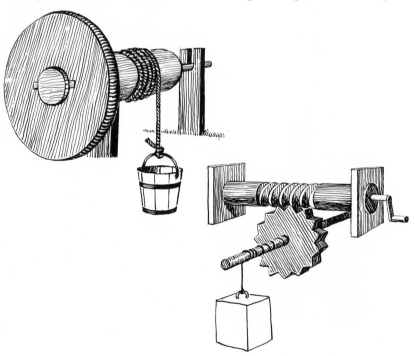

equal to that of several men. Archimedes explained the action by saying that a large wheel overpowers a small one. The lower device (page 24) reminds us of the gears used so much in modern machinery. This gear action gave a powerful pull when attached to the wheel and axle. In it, the toothed wheel was turned by the advancing spiral-shaped ridge of the upper attachment. For every complete turn of the crank handle, the toothed wheel moved the distance of one tooth.

The simple pulley had long been in use on boats and in the shipbuilding of the Mediterranean area. Archimedes has

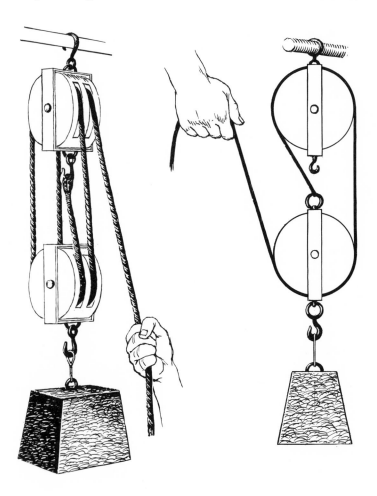

been given credit for the invention of two different pulley arrangements by which much stronger pulls could be exerted on ropes and cables by the strength of a single person. In the left-hand arrangement (page 25), one man is given the pulling strength of four; in the right-hand arrangement he has the strength of three. Archimedes sensed the mathematical relations between the number of strands of rope, the number of wheels, and the power achieved, but did not account for them.

The Great Demonstration

The inventions of Archimedes in the field of great forces might have gone unnoticed had it not been for the Great Demonstration that one legend tells us he put on for King Hiero.

The story behind the demonstration was told by Roman writers two centuries later. From their accounts, we may suppose that King Hiero had stopped in at the workshop to see what was new. Archimedes jokingly remarked that he was working on something that was really powerful. "Give me another earth on which to stand and a stout enough cable, and I by my own strength—with the help of my devices—can move the earth." The King did not seem interested. So Archimedes changed his suggestion. "Or I, sitting on the beach with my devices beside me, can—with just my own strength—draw the heaviest ship that ever sailed into the harbor of Syracuse out of its mooring place in the harbor upon the beach at my feet." The King declared the feat completely impossible. Archimedes smiled and declared that it was fully possible.

A demonstration was called for. A heavy framework was built on the shore, the framework being attached solidly to posts sunk in the sand. The devices Archimedes would be using were set in place: The rope from the drum of the wheel and axle was attached to one of the new pulley arrangements, and from the pulley terminus a cable was run to a big boat in the harbor.

We can imagine the events. A holiday was declared, and the boat was crowded with the guests invited for the occasion. The people of Syracuse lined the shore. The King was on the shore beside Archimedes. The signal was given; the ship's anchor was raised. Archimedes, half crouching on the sand, began to turn the crank handle. As the crank went on turning, the drum and pulley wheels groaned under the strain of the tightening rope and cable. Then, slowly but steadily, by the strength of a single man, the loaded boat began to move across the harbor. As it neared the sandy shore, Archimedes turned the crank handle over to the King, who brought the vessel to its landing, in the ovation that followed. One Roman writer quotes the King as saying, "After this, we shall believe anything that Archimedes tells us."

Archimedes' story has a violent ending. In 212 B.C., the Romans under their general, Marcellus, captured Syracuse. For three years the city defenses had held out. During those years, catapults designed by the great inventor had hurled rocks from the city walls upon the Roman boats. Missile-shooting contrivances devised by him had killed soldiers attacking the walls by land. But even more terrifying, from the Roman standpoint, was a special war machine produced by Archimedes and his assistant that Marcellus himself described. It could run a long beam out from the wall by the harbor with a bronze claw at its end. The claw would suddenly be dropped into the prow of a boat filled with soldiers in armor. It would clutch the boat and then, with an upward jerk, upend it and spill the soldiers to drown in the water.

Eventually the city was taken and ruthlessly destroyed. In that destruction, a Roman officer and his followers burst into the workshop where the old man, then seventy-five, was apparently preparing a mold in the sand for the bronze casting of some new engine of war. "Don't touch that curve!" are said to have been Archimedes' last words before a soldier killed him with his spear.

Galileo Galilei

CHAPTER 2

Galileo:
The Making of a Scientist

Galileo Galilei, one of the great pioneers of physics, was born in Pisa, Italy, in 1564. That was almost eighteen centuries after the death of Archimedes—a long period of time in human history. In those centuries, Rome grew from a small military power to a great empire, and after several centuries of expanding power the empire collapsed. Later, a Moslem empire, originating in Arabia, spread across three continents. Eventually, this empire, too, lost its importance and power. Next, the Italian cities of Venice, Genoa, Milan, and Florence rose to world prominence. By 1564, the importance of these cities was fading, while certain Western European port cities facing the Atlantic gained in prosperity as the lands of the New World were opened to commerce and settlement.

Those eighteen centuries were not a period of steady advance in civilization. Progress was halted several times by the forces of destruction. Science and invention had also lost ground in the days of devastation. But now, with Galileo, the advance of knowledge would begin again.

University Days

At seventeen, Galileo was enrolled in the University of Pisa, through his father's efforts, to attend lectures on medicine. Pisa did not have the oldest of Italian universities, nor the most renowned, but it was rated as a good school. When he entered the university, these were Galileo's qualifications: He was healthy and strong, and had an active and alert mind. He liked music, was good at sketching, and could paint well in oils. He was able to quote from memory long passages of poetry, and could speak in public in a pleasing manner. On the other hand, Galileo had never studied geometry or simple algebra, and had never attended a class in science, which would certainly bar him from entering any medical school today.

The details of his early studies are not known. His parents were probably very happy in their belief that Galileo, their oldest son, would become a great and famous physician. His first years at the university were full of promise. But his medical training was never completed, and in the autumn of his fourth year of study he stopped attending classes.

An early incident at Pisa had set the stage for the happenings of that final year. In the spring of his first year at the university, Galileo started out to attend a public lecture. By error he walked into the wrong room and found that he was listening to a discussion of some problems in advanced geometry. Unable to leave without embarrassment, the young student remained in his seat. He knew nothing about the subject, but the lecturer must have aroused his curiosity and his interest, for he borrowed some student-written notes on elementary geometry for the summer.

In his spare time during the next two university years, he used borrowed notes to study a brief course in algebra and then an advanced treatise on geometry that included the handling of such curves as the ellipse, parabola, and helix. He did not enroll in these classes and took no part in discussion groups.

Both the geometry and the algebra were probably easy for him to understand, but there is nothing to indicate that he found either subject thrilling before the day he discovered in nature a new kind of curve that did not appear in earlier mathematical writings.

The Path of the Ribbon

We have no reliable information, but we can imagine what happened. From the grassy banks of the Arno River, which goes through Pisa on its way westward to the sea, he may, in the spring of his third year at the university, have been idly watching the carts that crossed the river bridge. The wheel of one cart had a band of colored ribbon tied to its rim. The lad supposed that the ribbon would move along at the same speed as the cart, but it did not behave that way. The band could be down in the dust of the road, almost motionless. Then it seemed to leap up suddenly. Next, at the top of the wheel, it dashed forward faster than the cart itself. Then, suddenly dropping, it was back in the road again. He took out his sketch pad and in a series of simple sketches tried to show the ribbon's path, but all too quickly the cart had passed over the bridge and was gone.

A day or so later, Galileo took a wheel and fastened a crayon next to its rim to represent the ribbon. He placed the wheel beside the garden wall. As it revolved, the crayon traced the ribbon's path upon the wall. It was a strange curve. Galileo, certain that he was the discoverer of something never seen before, named it the *cycloid curve.*

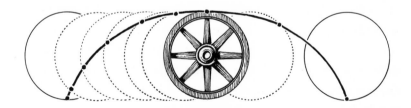

Science with Archimedes

When summer came, and vacation days with it, Galileo visited an elderly scholar of Florence. He probably told the scholar about his wonderful new curve. The old man, finding that he had an interested listener, talked with the young student for several days about Archimedes' scientific work. Young Galileo had known only about the Greek scientist's contributions to mathematics. The Florentine scholar told the boy that some of Archimedes' important science treatises had been preserved down through the centuries by being translated from the original Greek into Arabic, the language of the Moslems. These translations had been used by the scholars in the great universities of the Moslem portion of Spain. Quite recently, he said, the Arabic versions had been translated into Latin, and had been published as books.

The summer was partially gone before Galileo had a chance to see the Latin translation of Archimedes' short report on bodies that float and bodies that sink. After the autumn classes had started at Pisa, he read a report about Archimedes' solution to the problem of the King's crown. From a scientific standpoint it was not a satisfactory report, since it referred only vaguely to the equipment used and the steps of the experiment. Much was left to the imagination. Galileo, after carefully studying what was written, made sketches of the equipment that Archimedes might have used.

First, he repeated the boat experiments suggested by Archimedes; there were no problems. But when the young scientist set up some equipment for performing the crown experiment, he was immediately confronted by the need to find something made entirely or largely of gold to substitute for the crown. He finally decided to use the signet ring given to him by his father. A jeweler may have said that it was probably three-fourths gold and one-fourth silver, the silver being added for hardness and wearability. The ring was so small, however, that weighing the overflow water as the ring was submerged would be too inaccurate.

Galileo decided to make use of Archimedes' idea, already mentioned, that when a body heavier than water is weighed in water, its weight will be lighter than its true weight by the weight of the water displaced. It would not be necessary to weigh the water that was displaced; he could find its exact weight as Archimedes would have done, by seeing how much lighter the ring became when submerged in water.

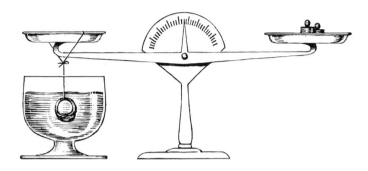

Using a balance, Galileo weighed his ring as it hung from a loop of thread stretched across one of the scale pans. Then he placed a jar of water under the scale pan, and, with the ring submerged in the water, weighed it again. Had the ring been pure gold, it would have weighed 19 times that of an equal volume of water. Silver is about 10½ times heavier than water. When he divided the weight of the signet ring by that of the displaced water, it turned out to be 17½ times as heavy as water. By arranging the three numerical values in a row—19 (for gold); 17½ (for the ring); 10½ (for silver)—Galileo saw that the ring's weight was closer to that of gold than to that of silver. Indeed, it was three-fourths gold and one-fourth silver, as the jeweler had predicted. Galileo had discovered a way by which the purity of a gold ring could be determined in a minute or so, accurately and completely, without harm to the ring. The same plan could be used for a coin or any small object. True, the idea was Archimedes', but the application was new. Galileo called his arrangement a *hydrostatic balance*.

All this work took time—the studying of each treatise, the devising of experiments, the work on his hydrostatic balance. He neglected his studies and stopped attending lectures. After that, lacking enough money to go on, he withdrew from the University of Pisa without receiving a degree, and returned to his family home, in Florence. Galileo tried to explain to his father what had happened. "I am about to become as famous as the great Archimedes," he insisted over and over.

At home in Florence, he remained so excited about the work of Archimedes and his own hydrostatic balance that for half a year he made no attempt to find any moneymaking work. Instead, he studied mathematics, as his father, who was a mathematician, encouraged him to do, and he wrote a short treatise on the hydrostatic balance.

Contradicting Aristotle

In 1589, when Galileo was twenty-five, he secured, through the timely assistance of an influential family friend, a teaching position at the University of Pisa. The post was a poorly paid minor lectureship in poetry and painting; in addition Galileo taught a single class in geometry for which few students applied. When he accepted, he thought that the lecture work would be interesting and pleasant. But Galileo retained this lecture position for only two years.

The medical faculty did not forget that he had failed to attend their lectures, and some of his former professors remembered that he had occasionally been hostile to the teachings of Aristotle, whom they favored. This Greek teacher and philosopher of two thousand years before had written on a multitude of topics. Galileo was primarily interested in Aristotle's discussions of science. In one passage dealing with weight, Aristotle stated that the velocity acquired by a falling body is proportional to the weight of the body. Galileo had his doubts about this. It would mean that if a stone was crushed into fragments, they would no longer all fall in the same amount of time. A piece twice as heavy as another would fall twice as fast, so the separate portions of the stone would be widely spaced out as they fell. Galileo may have gone to a bridge on the Arno and dropped stone fragments into the water below. One fragment would fall very much like another, no matter what its weight. Surely Aristotle was wrong.

In studying the careful work of Archimedes, Galileo had assumed that Aristotle was a poor experimenter. On the whole, this was not the case. Aristotle's conclusions were faulty, not his observations. In the case of his experiments on falling bodies, Aristotle had possibly dropped rounded stones of different weights from the top of the wall approaching the Acropolis of Athens. This wall, guarding the way to the citadel, was built along the front edge of a rocky slope. From the base of the wall, the slope extended outward and downward toward the sea. Ravines along the slope were partially filled with drifted sand. A stone dropped from the top of the wall would fall downward to the base of the wall, then bound down the rocky slope and finally be stopped by the obstructing sand.

The place chosen for the experiment might have had sand spreading smoothly down the slope. Aristotle may have observed that a stone twice as heavy as another went twice as far through the sand before stopping, and that three times as heavy a stone went three times as far. Perhaps from facts such as these, Aristotle came to his conclusions about the velocity of a falling body, for he may have assumed that the heavy body pushed its way farther through the obstructing sand because it entered the sand at a higher velocity. The assumption was wrong. The heavy body entered the sand with a greater driving force, not a greater velocity.

With the Aid of the Leaning Tower

In the city of Pisa, not far from the university, is the famous Leaning Tower, whose foundation settled to one side after the building was under construction. A doubtful legend tells us that Galileo performed a public demonstration here. To Galileo, the tower might have been a perfect setting for an experiment on how bodies really fall. Its height was 180 feet, there were eight stories with seven balustrades from which objects could be dropped, and the slope of the building made it possible for the objects to fall away from the base of the structure.

According to the story, an announcement appeared that Galileo Galilei would demonstrate at the noon hour, in front of the tower, that Aristotle had made an important error in reporting the behavior of falling bodies. Most of the students came, most of the faculty stayed away. The audience was told of Aristotle's statements that a heavy object falls faster than a light one. The audience was then informed that, at various tower balustrades, iron balls of different weights would be dropped in pairs. The observers were to note whether Aristotle was right.

The experiment went off smoothly. When released, each pair of iron weights started together, fell side by side, and hit the ground almost simultaneously. The results were convincing. Aristotle had been wrong. Galileo expected praise for his accomplishment, but in this he was to be disappointed. The faculty was, in general, not interested in anything that would contradict the writings of Aristotle, which were the basis of many of their teachings.

Parabolas on the Garden Wall

The Leaning Tower experiment was supposedly performed in the spring of Galileo's first year of teaching. He would not have returned to Pisa for a second year if he could have avoided it. He had been attacked bitterly by the university authorities for his disparaging remarks about Aristotle.

It was probably in his second year of teaching that Galileo began his studies on the parabola, and this work changed the course of his life. Perhaps on a lonely morning walk he stopped to watch the sparkling effect of the early sunshine on the spray of a water fountain. He may have concluded that it was as if the drops carried tiny mirrors with which to flash back the sun's rays as they rose to the crest of their curved paths. Motion always fascinated Galileo, and he would have loitered near the fountain, trying to follow individual drops as they rose, reached the top, and then fell into the pool of the fountain. Strangely, he could follow the path better by watching the shadows on the water. Each drop was so nearly transparent that it could scarcely be seen, but its shadow was readily visible. However, the pattern was still confusing. Not all of the drops moved in the same type of curve, so he could not be certain what kind of path was being followed.

He may have decided to make a model of a fountain in order to satisfy his curiosity. It could be done by putting a tall water jar on the ledge of a garden wall. When the jar was filled with water, a tiny stream of water spurted sideways from a small opening near the jar's base. This miniature fountain threw a clear shadow in the sunlight. The water started out horizontally, then bent downward as its weight pulled it toward the earth. The curve seemed to be following the shape of half a *parabola*, but he could not be certain. Perhaps by experiment, Galileo found that a slight slap given to the side of the water jar would flip the drops sideways as they were leaving the jar. By adjusting the position of the

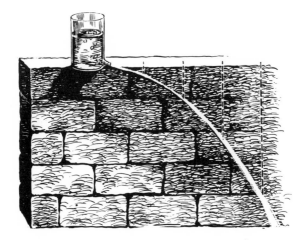

jar, he observed that the drops dampened the garden wall from their sideways motion, yet kept to the curve of their forward path. If he traced the curve on the wall before the dampness had evaporated, he could see that it was a parabola—a perfect parabola. That was a discovery; no writer had ever mentioned that this type of curve could be made in such a simple way.

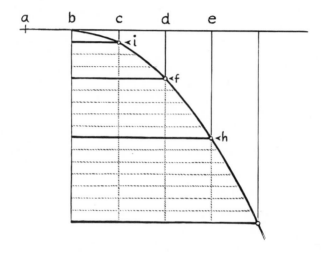

After that, Galileo probably drew many similar curves on the garden wall. For some of these he modified the size of the opening at the jar's base. For others, he changed the water depth, finding that the deeper the water, the more forcefully it spurted out. From these various curves, he probably selected one to be transferred to paper so he could study it more completely. On the drawing, a horizontal line was added at the top of the curve; four equal spaces were marked off on it and lettered a, b, c, d, and e. He extended dotted lines downward from these points to the curve, using i, f, and h to indicate the vertical lines.

Galileo was following a plan that Archimedes had used in studying the mathematics of parabolas. If line df should turn out to be exactly four times as long as line ci, and eh nine times as long as ci, then the figure matched the parabola of Archimedes.

The results checked perfectly. For his curve, the horizontal line represented *time*, the vertical ones were for the falling distances of objects. Galileo interpreted the parabola in this way, and formulated what we call the *Law of Falling Bodies:* The distance a body falls is proportional to the square of time of falling. That is, object *c*, which took three times longer to fall than *a*, traveled nine times as far.

Galileo's first curve was only half that of Archimedes'. He may have obtained the other half by aiming the stream of water diagonally upward; the curve would reach its top position, and then fall back toward the earth again. The two parts of the curve were alike, thus making Archimedes' parabola.

The results were wonderfully exciting to the young scientist. This time he did not make the mistake of announcing his findings at a public demonstration. That could wait. Instead, he would prepare a complete mathematical report, have it printed, and see that a copy reached every outstanding mathematician in Italy. He might even add something about the practical importance of this new study in relation to projectiles. A month after reaching these decisions, Galileo went home for the summer. His father, he found, was gravely ill (he was to die a few months later).

The son immediately wrote to Pisa, resigning his position at the university. While with his family in Florence, he had the report on his parabola studies printed and sent to mathematicians and scholars. He spoke at a public meeting on the need for a study of parabolas by those who used projectiles as weapons. Galileo gave a special lecture on the contributions of Archimedes to science. In a small book, to which he gave the title of *La Bilancetti (The Little Balance),* he explained how the Greek scientist might have performed his famous experiment on the King's crown, and he demonstrated his hydrostatic balance as a practical way by which the purity of gold coins could be checked quickly and accurately. Hearing that there was a vacancy on the faculty of the University of Padua, he applied for it.

Galileo at Padua

In the autumn of 1592, at the age of twenty-eight, Galileo was appointed professor of mathematics at Padua—a very important position for so young a man. The Italian city of Padua is near Venice, and its university was already old and famous. It had an outstanding faculty, and its students came from virtually every country in Western Europe.

His original appointment, at a good salary, was for six years. Later he was reappointed to two six-year periods, each time with a salary increase. During the eighteen years Galileo spent at Padua, he sent money regularly to his mother as long as she lived, and completed a sister's dowry that his father had initiated. He was happy in his work, and had a laboratory of his own where he engaged in epoch-making research. Always a good lecturer, he was now a brilliant one, and his lectures were always crowded with many enthusiastic students.

The Incident of the Swinging Lamp

The first research Galileo carried out in Padua enlarged upon some brief experiments he had made in Pisa about ten years before, when he had been a first-year medical student. We may imagine a lecturing physician reporting to his class that an abnormal pulse rate is a sign of possible illness. He may have explained that a doctor compared the pulse rate of a patient with his own in testing for abnormality. Perhaps Galileo wondered how the physician could know that his own pulse was normal, or whether his pulse rate agreed with that of other medical students. He probably found considerable variation. Whose pulse rate, then, should be considered normal?

A short time later, according to another doubtful legend, the young student is said to have had an experience that did not appear at the time to be related in any way to the human pulse beat or its measurement. During a Sunday-morning service in the Cathedral of Pisa, Galileo noticed that the great bronze lamp, which hung as a pendulum from the high-vaulted ceiling, was in gentle motion. It had apparently been left swinging when the lamp was refilled with oil. He counted his pulse beats in order to time the slow back-and-forth movement. At the close of the service, he timed the swings of the lamp again. Each one seemed to be taking the same time as before, though the back-and-forth distance through which the lamp moved was now less than it had been during his first count. The next morning, before going to class, he stepped into the Cathedral. The lamp was still in motion, though only slightly. To his surprise the duration of each swing was unchanged.

That day he did not want to go to classes; he had some important experimenting to do. In his room he made a simple pendulum from a piece of lead tied to a length of thread, and hung the pendulum in the open doorway. He made the thread about three feet long, and noticed that each swing took only slightly less time than one pulse beat. He tried pulling the lead back farther before releasing it. Again he used his pulse rate as a timing device; the change had an effect on the time of the pendulum's swing only when the lead was drawn back abnormally far. Then Galileo experimented with shortening and lengthening the pendulum thread. He found that a long pendulum swings at a slower rate than a short one does.

An idea now occurred to him. Why not set up a pendulum in the medical building, its length adjusted so that the time of its swing was the same as that of the head physician's pulse rate? Then the students could check their own pulse without disturbing the physician. He demonstrated the idea to the medical faculty; some of the professors liked the idea and used it.

More Experiments with the Pendulum

Galileo did not pursue his study of the pendulum any further until the year he went to Padua. For more advanced work, a knowledge of both algebra and geometry would be needed to understand the mathematical relation between the length of a pendulum and the time of its swing. In that first year at Pisa, Galileo had no understanding of these subjects; nor was he as yet a skillful experimenter. That would come later. But the greatest difficulty lay in the fact that he had no accurate way to measure small time intervals. He had used his pulse beat, though he was aware that excitement or brisk exercise would hurry its rate. For periods of time as long as an hour, he could use an hourglass made by the skilled Venetian glassworkers. When this device was turned upside down, the fine sand took just an hour to run from the glass container on the top through a narrow opening into the one at the bottom. But there was no way by which one minute could be measured accurately.

By the time Galileo went to Padua, he was a skilled mathematician and had also worked out in his mind just what he could do to measure small units of time accurately. His time-measuring

arrangement may remind us of the way he studied the parabolas on the garden wall. A water tank was set up, with a narrow exit tube at the bottom that could be opened or closed with the finger. The water running out was to be caught and weighed. To keep an even level of water in the tank, an overflow pipe was placed near its top, and any surplus water ran out of the pipe. In carrying out an experiment on the timing of a pendulum, the finger was removed from the exit pipe as the pendulum was released. The water was permitted to flow for at least twenty swings, then the finger again stopped up the pipe's opening.

At Padua, Galileo was assisted by enthusiastic students. First, they centered all efforts upon finding any relation between the length of a pendulum and its rate of swing. This was done by conducting many experiments, in which a variety of different pendulum lengths were used, and the water caught in each run was weighed. The lengths and weights were then put down side by side and examined to discover, if possible, any natural pattern. It was found very quickly that a pendulum twice as long as another did not have a swing double the time of the first, but that a pendulum four times as long did. Actually, nine times as long a pendulum had three times as long a time of swing; a pendulum sixteen times as long as another took four times longer for each swing. Galileo stated the results in this way: The time of swing of a pendulum is proportional to the square root of its length.

These experiments were followed by many others. In one, for example, he tried to devise a pendulum length so that one swing would take exactly one second. When this pendulum was constructed and checked experimentally, it became as easy to measure time as it was to measure length or volume. It is reported that the students in one of Galileo's classes went around with a piece of lead and a measured thread—making a "seconds pendulum"—that they used to time how long a person could hold his breath, or how long a choir could hold the last note of the

"Amen." In another set of experiments it was shown that if a falling piece of metal goes 16 feet 1 inch in the first second, it goes four times that far in the first two seconds. Or, if the metal was tossed to a height of 16 feet 1 inch, only to fall back to earth again, the total time would be just two seconds—one second for the rise, the other second for the descent.

There were still more pendulum experiments, for Galileo's curiosity and keen thinking resulted in a whole new line of experiments. As anyone knows, a heavy metal object hanging on a string will swing back and forth for a much longer time than a ping-pong ball on a string. It did not seem possible that the difference in behavior was entirely due to the weight difference. Galileo checked on the matter. Years later, Isaac Newton did, too. Newton took three hollow balls of the same size, stuffing the first with a pound of metal pieces, the second with a pound of wood scraps, and the third with a pound of feathers compressed into a compact mass. The three balls were fitted out with equal lengths of thread, and set swinging as pendulums. You might think that the ball with the metal in it will swing longest, the one with wood not as long, and the one with feathers a shorter time than either of the others. But you would be wrong: The swinging is just alike for all three. Now, when the three substances are out in the open at the end of a string, the metal-tipped pendulum will swing the longest period of time, the wood-tipped one a shorter time, and the feather-tipped pendulum will make a very few swings and stop. The great difference in the two experiments is due to air resistance.

Galileo was able to determine this from his own experiments. His argument, which was clear and concise, ran something like this: The air that surrounds the earth does not seem to weigh anything. But it does have some weight, so a force is needed to push aside the air as the pendulum passes back and forth through it. The force so used cuts down on the moving velocity of the object, and eventually it will stop. Exposed to the air, the metal tip of a pendulum is small in size and pushes aside but little air as it swings; its moving velocity is only slightly reduced. A feather-tipped pendulum, on the other hand, pushes aside a great amount of air with its fluffy mass; its velocity is greatly reduced, so the pendulum soon stops. A wood-tipped device disturbs more air in its motion than the metal and less than the feathers. Its velocity decreases more rapidly than the first and more slowly than the second.

Simple as the explanation seems today, it was a great achievement to recognize the part played by the obstructing force of air. Referring to falling bodies as they dash downward through the air, he also stated that a piece of lead and a mass of feathers should fall at exactly the same rate in a long tube having no air in it. Again he could not prove the matter by experiment. However, after the air pump was invented, one of the first experiments tried with it proved that Galileo had been right. In a tube that was without air, the lead and the feathers dropped at the same rate.

Correcting the Errors of Aristotle

The story of Galileo's correction of Aristotle's error about the velocity of falling bodies has already been told. Galileo also made other corrections in Aristotle's work.

From the Acropolis hill in Athens, Aristotle could quite clearly see the sailing boats in the harbor. He could tell when the wind stopped blowing in the harbor, for then the sails would sag and the boats stop. Perhaps with this in mind, he wrote: It is the *natural condition* for any object to be *at rest*. A force is needed to make a body move. When that force is removed, the body stops. Galileo's statement about the natural condition of objects was very different; it was correct, and Aristotle's was wrong. Galileo realized that a body in motion tends to keep on in motion, and with the same velocity. A body at rest tends to remain at rest. A force is needed to change the velocity of a moving body, or to stop a body, or to set it into motion. Now the name for this natural tendency to keep going or to remain motionless is called *inertia.*

What error had Aristotle made? He assumed that the boat stopped by itself when the wind stopped blowing. Actually, it would have tended to keep on going, but the obstructing force of the water halted it. In connection with moving things, Aristotle made another error. He knew that an arrow shot horizontally kept on going forward as well as downward, and he supposed that the air around the arrow was pushing the object on. (We would agree with Galileo that the arrow kept moving on because there was no retarding force.) Aristotle declared that solids and liquids fall downward, while air and fire rise. Galileo said that air, like solids and liquids, has weight, though the weight is not large, and so the arrow would have to fall. He was uncertain about fire.

What has here been said about the work of Galileo at Padua is but a small portion of what he contributed to science in those eighteen years at the university. Actually in that time he created a whole new division of the science of physics—*mechanics,* the study of energy and forces and their effects on bodies. Moreover, he had heard about the invention of the telescope in Holland, and in 1609 he set about making some of these instruments. Within the year he had been so successful in his refinements that he was able to construct the first astronomical telescope. In January of 1610, Galileo became the first man to observe four of the satellites of the planet Jupiter. Later, he also observed the rings of Saturn, the phases of Venus, the broken surface of the moon, and sunspots. Another of his discoveries was that the Milky Way was a vast aggregation of stars. A number of observations confirmed his belief that the earth and other planets revolve in orbits around the sun, and that the earth was therefore not the center of the universe. For the rest of his life, Galileo was bitterly assailed for his convictions about astronomy, which appeared to shake the foundations of the religious thought of the time.

In 1610, at the age of 46, Galileo resigned from his position at Padua. He had found a rich sponsor, Cosimo II, Grand Duke of Tuscany. The Duke appointed Galileo his mathematician and philosopher. The financial support of Cosimo II offered Galileo an increased opportunity to continue his scientific labors. Moreover, he had a nostalgic longing for Florence, for a home with a pleasant garden, singing birds, and shadows among the trees. He acquired a home like that after he left Padua, and a scientific workshop where, with trained assistants, he went on with his experiments. He also maintained a voluminous correspondence with his students and others. In 1610, then, the life story of Galileo started a fresh chapter, which will be taken up later in connection with his scientific achievements in the fields of heat and light.

Isaac Newton

CHAPTER 3

Young Isaac Newton

Galileo died in Italy early in the year 1642, at the age of 78. Later in that year another great physicist, Isaac Newton, was born at Woolsthorpe Manor, a farm in Lincolnshire, England, near the village of Grantham. The farm had a broad sweep of pasture land and was crossed by a brook whose water flowed leisurely off toward the east and the distant shores of the North Sea.

Isaac was a tiny, premature baby, born after his father's death. At six he was still small and frail. He was a gentle, serious lad whose face would occasionally light up with a wonderful smile. At seventeen he was a slender lad of nearly normal height but without the muscular strength needed to handle a plow in spring, to dig drainage ditches in summer, or to toss bags of grain into carts in the autumn. He was not robust enough to become a farmer. Something would have to be done about the farm and about young Isaac himself, and his mother's brother asked to be permitted to hire a farmhand to do the heavy work of the Manor. He wished also to pay the boy's fees for a year at Trinity College, in Cambridge University.

Isaac did not attend the village school at Grantham until he was twelve. Before that time he no doubt helped around the house, followed his grandmother to the vegetable garden, and looked for nests that the farm hens hid along the hedgerows. A relative of his by marriage, John Conduitt, has told how he rose from last place in his class to first place. There was a bully in the class, who was also getting better grades than Isaac. One day, the bully "as they were going to school gave him a kick in the belly which put him to a great deal of pain. When school was over Newton challenged him to a fight, and they went into the church-yard. . . . Isaac Newton had the more spirit and resolution, and beat him till he would fight no more. . . . Determined to beat him also at his books, by hard work he finally succeeded, and then gradually rose to be the first in the school."

Ghostly Lanterns of the Sky

When Newton was fourteen or fifteen, his hands and wrists were strong enough for him to do wood carving. And, like many another boy of that day and this, he designed and built contrivances out of wood. Probably wooden windmills came first, then waterwheels turned by the meadow brook. A little later he constructed his first "invention." It was a counting device and was attached to the heavy farm cart to record the number of revolutions a wheel made as the cart moved along the country roads.

Like other boys, he made kites, and these led him to his second invention. He took a sheet of heavy paper, stiffened it with starch paste, and, before the paste dried, shaped the paper to match the curves of a bird's outspread wings. To get his "bird" into the sky, he made two holes in the paper figure and passed a kite string through the openings. Then he went out on the pasture hill to see whether the bird would move up the unreeled kite string when the wind blew. The paper figure moved a short way up, then stopped. Thinking that a paper boat built in the same way would catch the wind with its sails and so fly higher, he built one. If the wind was blowing strongly enough, up the kite string went the boat. After that, Isaac put a small candle in the paper boat. He waited until night to try out a plan that had come to his mind.

The story is still told in Lincolnshire of young Newton and the strange candlelighted object that one evening seemed to leap the pasture fence, climb jerkily above the orchard trees, dive toward the roof of his house, and finally peep into the bedroom window. According to the tale, his mother screamed, and his grandfather grabbed his gun. But when Newton's grandmother boldly stepped outside, the ghostly lantern carrier was vanishing over the field; only she seems to have sensed that her grandson had anything to do with the matter.

Newton's Laws of Motion

These experiments were interesting to the boy, but his mind was soon following new trails. Perhaps he began to think about the tugging force of a kite string when the kite was flying. He may have wondered why the string appeared to be pulling just as hard on his finger as on the kite. If the string broke, the pull on his finger and the pull on the kite stopped at exactly the same time. Did that mean there were two forces at work, identical as twins, pulling in opposite directions? Possibly a single force was acting between two bodies—his hand and the kite—drawing them toward each other. Then Newton may have thought about other forces. Sometimes objects were pushed apart, sometimes they were pulled together. Magnetism was a force; two north poles repelled one another while a north pole and a south pole were attracted by magnetic force. Magnetism did not affect a single body; there were always two objects that were acted upon. He may have wondered if there might also be a force that could act upon a single object only.

Perhaps he started looking for forces at work. Then he may have decided that he was not interested in a force itself but in whether it acted upon two objects, and whether the action on the two was equal in size but opposite in direction. In a short time he could have found many examples to study. When the farm horse started to run on a muddy road, the mud was pushed backward, the horse forward. If his grandfather had told him not to jump from the top of an empty barrel that had been closed at the top and set aside, he may have wondered why he should not do this. Perhaps he got the cat upon such an empty barrel and then called to it. As it leaped, the light barrel tipped over backward, and the cat landed in a heap on the floor. The action of the animal's muscles had been the force, and its actions were opposite and doubtless equal.

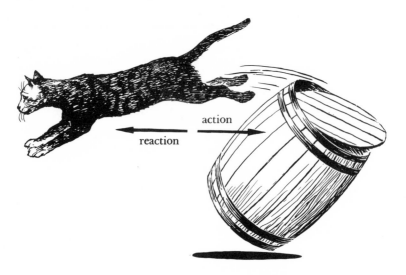

During these pre-college years, Newton apparently studied geometry by himself. He may also have heard of Galileo's work in mechanics. And he probably began to jot down his thoughts in a notebook. Many years later, these early ideas developed into his famous *Three Laws of Motion*, which may be summarized as follows:

Law 1. A body at rest tends to remain at rest; a body in motion tends to continue in motion.

Law 2. A force acting upon a body is equal to the body's rate of change of momentum.

Law 3. Every action has an equal and opposite reaction.

Lessons from a Whirling Pail

Some of Newton's boyhood experiences on the farm may have supported his theories about motion. Like all farm boys, he probably knew that a pail of water would not spill if it was whirled fast enough in a circle around the body. The cord attached to the pail's handle would pull with an outward force on the hand and an equal inward one on the pail. The names of these two actions are derived from Latin. The outward action is called *centrifugal* ("flying from the center") *force*. The other is *centripetal* ("seeking the center") *force*.

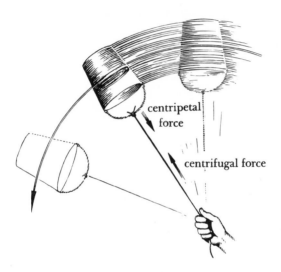

centripetal force

centrifugal force

Young Newton might have thought that the pail, if released should go straight away from him, for the centrifugal force was outward—but it does not. It goes off to one side, spilling water as it travels. To understand what was happening, he could have tried a simple experiment at a flat, sandy place along a brook. Instead of using the pail, he could fasten a piece of iron at the end of a somewhat longer cord. Whirling the iron in a circle, just touching the surface of the sand, he could let the cord suddenly slip out of his grasp. The released iron would

not move outward; it would take a straight-line path toward *B* in the sketch. This line is called the *tangent* of the circle.

The figure in the sand shows applications of all three of Newton's laws of motion. According to Law 1, force is needed to pull the moving metal into a curved path; when the force stops the metal goes straight on in the new direction it has been taking. The second law requires that a more powerful force is needed to swing a heavier weight or one on a shorter cord than to swing a light weight or one on a longer cord. According to the third law, the centrifugal and the centripetal forces disappear at the same time.

It is doubtful that Newton had mentioned his findings to anyone, even his own family, when he went to Trinity College. To his teacher and classmates in the village school he was a bright lad, quick with numbers and rather inventive, but they never dreamed that he would be considered a genius.

An Unexpected Vacation

In the fall of 1665, Newton had completed his regular college work and was continuing his studies when a terrible epidemic of bubonic plague broke out in London, and people died there by the thousands. England was panic-stricken at the news. Cambridge University was closed, and all members of the university, including Isaac Newton, were sent home and urged to stay away from city streets. They were told that the university would reopen when the danger was over.

In the quiet of Woolsthorpe, Newton found the time to think about many of the scientific problems of the time. At home there was no farm work that he could do. Smiling, he probably told his mother that he would be a boarder, and a very lazy one. For the first few days he was content to lie in the shade on the orchard slope, idly watching the clouds as they drifted leisurely across the sky, but he could not be completely idle for very long.

Within two years he demonstrated his originality and thinking ability by developing the *binomial theorem* of algebra, and by finding a method for the calculation of the area within the *hyperbola,* a curve that, like the parabola, is a conic section. He also invented an approach to a new division of mathematics that he called "fluxions"; it is known today as the *calculus* and deals with processes involving limits, such as problems of velocity, acceleration, and the slope of curves.

During these years Newton also continued his thinking about gravitation. He may have found, stored away among his other boyhood treasures, the notebooks set aside five years before, when he had first gone off to Cambridge. Perhaps he glanced over them—then looked at the written records of his youthful ideas more carefully. They seemed sound. With his greater mathematical insight, he now could see how various points in the old notes could be enlarged upon. He was particularly interested in the notes on the laws of motion, as well as in the material on centrifugal and centripetal forces. He went out to the orchard and, sitting under an apple tree, continued his thoughts.

Scientific Thoughts Under the Apple Tree

Years later, when Newton was asked how "the notion of gravitation came into his mind," he replied: "It was occasioned by the fall of an apple, as I sat in a contemplative mood." Later on, storytellers enlarged on this remark by saying that Isaac Newton's ideas on gravitation began after he was hit on the head by a falling apple. This half-joking remark has often been repeated as if it were true, or of importance.

Newton was never to explain fully in a step-by-step manner how he reached his great conclusions about gravitation. We do know, of course, that his thinking was associated with the orchard slope of his home on some warm afternoons in the summer of 1666. No laboratory experiments were needed or performed. To get an understanding of how his ideas developed, let us imagine ourselves with Newton, listening as he talks to himself about force and motion, apples and moons, tides and gravity. This is fiction, but it may give a clue to how his thinking spanned the gap from the forces at work on the earth to the heavenly bodies and their motions.

" 'A body at rest remains at rest unless acted upon by some force.' The idea appears correct. But does not the wording imply that a lack of motion always comes from a lack of force? Is that idea correct? Six years ago I placed a rock on the top of a hill. If it is still there, it has been motionless for six years. Tomorrow, or some other day, that rock may go rolling down and come to rest at the bottom of the hill. Now, if a lack of motion comes from a lack of force, the rock was without it for six years, then suddenly had force applied to it as it started down the hill. At the bottom of the hill the force was withdrawn again—it was *weight*.

"But is weight really turned on and off? Is it not always present? If it is always there, the rock, when at rest for six years, had the downward force of weight exactly balanced by some force directed upward. Then, the rock as it is in motion down the hill may be acted upon only by the unbalanced weight force or by a combination of unbalanced forces. That explanation seems reasonable."

An apple falls to the ground near him. He reaches over to pick it up. "When an apple falls, the holding power of the tree lets go. The force of weight, no longer balanced, draws the apple toward the earth. But how tall would the tree need to be to get beyond the pull of this force? Of course, the force might go on, unchanged; it might have an upward border somewhere above the ground where it stops; or it might fade away gradually. Certainly this force reaches the tops of the earth's tallest mountains, for rockslides and avalanches move down the lofty slopes. But would it reach the moon?"

Now he opens his old notebook to a passage written just after he had experimented with whirling the metal weight around on a cord. "I wonder what the string is that holds the moon as it travels in a circular path around the earth. I can see nothing. I can feel nothing. But something very powerful is holding on to the moon, and that same powerful something must be pulling upward and outward upon the earth. That something would be the weight force of the moon—it must be. Then the earth's pull on bodies that we call weight extends out in space as far as the moon and possibly farther.

"It may seem strange to think of the pull of weight as being something like a string. What a tremendous number of separate strings would be needed! For this apple tree, thousands of such separate threads would be required—one at least for each apple, or twig, or leaf, or bit of bark. For such a large object as the moon, the separate strings that seem to be necessary would be beyond human comprehension."

He then returns to an earlier point. "With the moon held in place by the pull of its weight as directed toward the earth, it may be possible to calculate whether the weight of a ton on the earth's surface would be the same on the moon, or whether weight fades away with distance.

"Galileo's scientific work indicates that a body drops 16 feet in the first second of fall, and four times as far in two seconds. This is for an object at the earth's surface. The moon is 64 times as far from the earth's center as Galileo's object would be. For this calculation, he would have used 4,000 miles as the earth's radius and 250,000 miles as the distance to the moon. The moon is continually being pulled away from a straight-line path by the action of the weight force. It completes its orbit of the earth in 27.3 days. By using the 27.3 days and the 250,000 miles as the distance to the moon, it is possible, by geometry, to determine how many seconds elapse as the moon moves 16 feet away from the straight-line path, toward the earth. The answer comes out 64 seconds. The relation is simple. The moon is 64 times as far away from the center of the earth as an object on the earth's surface. But the time it takes the moon to fall through a space of 16 feet, as drawn away from its straight-line path, is 64 times as long as the same falling distance would take at the earth's surface.

"The mathematically simple relationship of distance and force indicates that the weight force fades away with distance in a completely predictable way. And it does not apply only to the earth; it extends far out into space."

Since the earth is a satellite of the sun, in traveling through its orbit it has to be pulled away from its straight-line path. If Newton could find the time, in seconds, that it would take to have the earth's path changed by 16 feet, he could see whether the moon and the earth both follow a similar plan.

The sun is 372 times farther away from the earth than the moon is. From the year's length and the distance from the earth to the sun, he calculated the time in seconds required to pull the earth 16 feet away from a straight-line path. This is just 372 times as long as the same pull takes the moon. The weight force fades away with distance, then, in a completely predictable manner, as before. Nature is a mathematician even far out into the heavens.

Up to this point we have been using the terms "weight" or "weight force" for the force acting upon apples and rocks falling to the earth, the moon pulled from its straight-line path by the earth, and the earth drawn from its straight-line path by the sun. Newton used the word *gravity,* from the Latin *gravitas* ("heaviness"), to mean the attraction between bodies wherever they are in the universe. *Weight* he used in connection with this earth and bodies drawn toward it.

The Law of Universal Gravitation

Later in that summer of 1666, Newton's thinking returned to the consideration of the moon. He knew that whenever the moon passes high over the North Sea, the particles of water in the sea rise to produce a *tide*. As the moon goes by, the lifting pull upon the water ceases and the particles settle back in position again. The force of gravitation that produces the rise of the tide acts upon more than just the top particles of water. For a mile-deep ocean, it reaches every particle in the column of water, with each particle pulled—as if by a thin colorless thread—as the moon is overhead and released as it passes on. The solid particles of the earth are also attracted by the moon's gravitational attraction, though tides in the earth can scarcely be noticed. The pull of the sun forms ocean tides, too, though the solar tides are

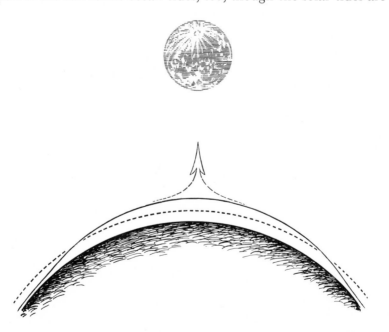

smaller than the lunar tides. So each water particle rises—again as if pulled by a thread—as the far-off sun traverses the sky. And each particle of the solid earth is also attracted to the sun. The threads of gravitational force are not like those of human manufacture. They never become tangled; they cannot be cut; they pass through intermediate substances as if there was nothing to stop them or shift their direction.

Now, thinking about the universe in all of its immensity, Newton stated that the force of gravity is not limited to this earth and the heavenly bodies closest to it. It exists everywhere. The universe, then, can be thought of as an orderly arrangement of heavenly bodies held in position and in orbit by the interplay of gravitational forces. This is the *Law of Universal Gravitation.*

In 1667 the plague was over and Trinity College reopened. Newton was appointed an instructor in mathematics at a regular salary. For the first time in his life, he would have money earned by his own efforts. During his stay at Woolsthorpe, Newton had not only made profound discoveries in mathematics and gravity but had perceived some very remarkable things about light and color as well. Now the work of Newton the scientist had begun. This will be discussed in the section on light.

PART II / *Widening the Scope of Physics*

Between the time of Galileo's great achievements and the time of Newton's work on force and motion, several young scientists, all influenced by Galileo's methods and accomplishments, broadened the scope of research and experimentation in physics.

Outstanding among these men were Evangelista Torricelli, of Italy; Blaise Pascal, of France; Otto von Guericke, of Germany; Robert Boyle, of England; and Gabriel Fahrenheit, of Germany and the Netherlands. This section deals with these men of physics.

Otto
von Guericke

Evangelista
Torricelli

Robert Boyle

Henry Cavendish

John Dalton

CHAPTER 4

Studies of the Atmosphere and of Gases

The Boy in the Alexandrian Barbershop

The time of Archimedes figures in the story of seventeenth-century science. Let us imagine that a very curious teen-age boy of Alexandria, in the second century B.C., the son of a prosperous barber, has been slipping into the barbershop on holidays, trying to make an organ that will play bird songs. His name is Ctesibius; it will be found in books on engineering, for he was to become noted as an inventor and builder.

Above the barber chair in that shop of long ago, there was probably a large mirror of polished silver suspended by a stout cord from the ceiling. The barber would reach up and pull the mirror down to show his customer the results when his work was completed. Then it would be pushed up again, out of the way. To permit the mirror to be handled in this way, the supporting cord was run over small wheels attached to the ceiling. At the wall, the cord was carried down to an opening in the top of a cabinet. At the rope's end was a hanging weight. It fitted the interior of the cabinet space closely, and rose when the mirror was pulled down by the barber, settling down again when the mirror was raised. In the base of the cabinet, below the hanging weight, there may have been a small crevice. Through this crevice, air would flow in when the weight went up, and out again as it fell. In its passage, the air hissed or sighed, depending on its speed in moving through the crevice. When the shop was empty, Ctesibius might have leaned over the cabinet with a hand on the cord above it and a finger at the crevice. By moving his finger back and forth over the opening, he may have been able to imitate bird chirps or the sound of wind with this device.

When the boy grew to manhood, he very likely experimented with the weight in the cabinet, and might, for example, have developed a practical air-moving machine such as the sketches show. A tightly fitting piston took the place of the counterpoise weight. A cylinder with an interior of smooth metal replaced the cabinet. What had been the crevice appeared as two air tubes facing each other at the base of the cylinder. Perhaps a new

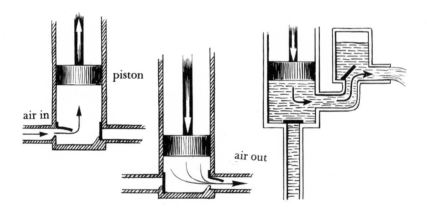

feature was added to Ctesibius's invention—a valve, operating like a trapdoor and made of leather, permitted the air to pass in one direction only through the air tubes at the base. When the piston was raised, the valve opened the left tube, and air went past it into the cylinder. When the piston was lowered, the valve opened the tube to the right, and the air rushed out.

There were few uses then for such an air-compressing device; today it would be good for inflating tires. One very important function was probably discovered by accident. Say that the left tube had settled into a pool of water; when the piston was moved up and down, the device threw water and mud through the exit tube. The next step was to turn the device into a *force pump*, as shown in the third sketch. The force with which the water was squirted through the nozzle depended upon the size of its opening and the rapidity of the piston strokes.

For untold centuries, water was drawn from shallow wells with such a pump. Then, about three and a half centuries ago in Germany, a new use was found for it. It became a fire-fighting device.

How von Guericke Produced a Vacuum with an Air Pump

In the seventeenth century, Otto von Guericke, an able scientist and an official of the city of Magdeburg, Germany, included in a book he wrote a picture of a pump that he had invented. The accompanying drawing, based upon Guericke's picture, also shows the interior of the pump, indicating its piston and valves. The lower part of the metal pump was passed at an angle through

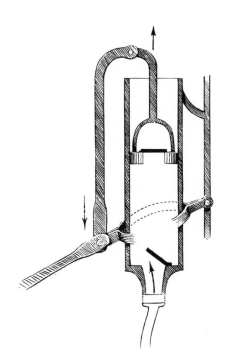

the side of a large oak barrel, the joint between pump and barrel being closed with washers and packing. Von Guericke wanted to use his pump to make a vacuum, so that he could study it. He had been going over the writings of Galileo, concentrating on the Italian scientist's conclusion that air was a retarding force in the motion of a pendulum, and his idea that a vacuum was merely a space without any air in it. The ancients had said that nature abhorred a vacuum, so things were sucked in by a vacuum, but was it not more probable that things were *pushed* into the space?

Guericke had been thinking that he could create a vacuum in the top of the barrel by filling it brimful with water, sealing all top openings tightly, and then pumping the water out. As the water level dropped, there should be a completely empty space left behind. The idea seemed excellent and very simple.

With the barrel filled with water and sealed, the pump was started, two men operating the piston. But air leaked in at the top with a hissing noise as water came out of the pump nozzle. The sealing had evidently been imperfect. Two more trials were made after greater care had been taken to plug up all locations where leaks had occurred. At the second of these trials, Guericke thought he had the vacuum that he wanted. But it did not *last*. Air was slowly working through the pores of the wood. He decided to use a metal container, and connected an air pump to a specially built copper sphere about two cubic feet in capacity. This time Guericke decided not to fill the sphere with water, but to pump out directly the air that filled it, thus leaving a vacuum. A *brass stopcock*—a faucetlike device—was inserted tightly at the top of the sphere, and a metal tube with a valve in it was inserted at the bottom. The stopcock could be opened to allow air to reenter and fill the container. The pump was attached to the lower connection. Guericke described what happened:

> *"At first the piston moved easily, but soon it became more difficult to move it, so that two strong men were hardly*

able to pull the piston out. While they were still occupied with pulling it in and out, and already believed that nearly all the air was drawn out, suddenly with a loud noise and to the astonishment of all the metal sphere was crushed in as a cloth can be rolled up between the fingers."

He blamed the collapse upon a defect in the container's construction, and had a second metal sphere made, with heavier walls, this time watching every step in the manufacture so that the resulting form would be a perfect sphere. When the air was pumped out, there was no collapse, and the pumping continued until air stopped coming from the nozzle. The valve between the pump and the sphere was closed. Now, what should be done with the vacuum? Guericke wrote:

"On opening the stopcock, the air rushed with such force into the copper sphere that it seemed as if it would draw in a man standing before it. If the face was brought fairly near, the breath was taken away and one could not hold one's hand above the stopcock without the risk that it would be violently drawn to it."

Later parts of his book describe how he perfected this way of obtaining a vacuum, as well as numerous experiments he performed. Those dealing with the weighing of air are of interest here. The sphere was weighed when full of air, and weighed again after the air was removed. The difference was the weight of the air that had been in the sphere; for example, 12 cubic feet of air near sea level weigh almost one pound. Guericke went beyond this and showed that a certain volume of heated air weighed less than an equal volume of cold air.

Those who heard about Guericke's experiments found the results completely surprising. They knew that air in motion had pressure, but they had no idea that air not in motion still exerted pressure, as had been shown when air rushed into the evacuated sphere once the stopcock was opened. Guericke was a showman, and in our time would be called a great popularizer of science. He staged an impressive demonstration. Special invitations were sent to princes and nobles, and seats were set up at the edge of a field beside the walls of Magdeburg. For the occasion, Guericke had had constructed two half-spheres, or hemispheres, of bronze with flanged parts so smooth and so perfectly tooled that the hemispheres, when placed one flange against the other, made a perfectly tight metal sphere. One hemisphere had a stopcock, the other the pipe-and-valve attachment that had been used in the earlier experiment. Each hemisphere had a stout handle fashioned from bronze. The arrangement made it possible for the equipment to be examined fully, to prove that no trickery was involved.

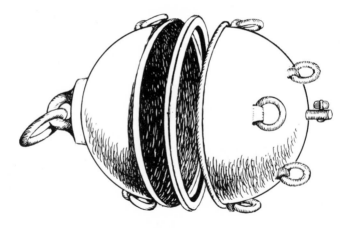

The climax of the performance came when the emptied sphere, held together by the force of the outside air trying to rush into the vacuum, could not be separated by the pulling force of sixteen horses—two teams of eight pulling against each other. After several trials, the horses were unhooked and led away. The two hemispheres, still locked together by the pressure on them of the outside air, were placed upon a table in full view of all the spectators. The official selected for the task now came forward. After stating what he was going to do, he turned the stopcock. With a prolonged sharp hiss, the air rushed in. Now the hemisphere could be pried apart.

How Torricelli Invented the Barometer

Although Guericke could demonstrate the existence of air pressure, his equipment could not conveniently measure that pressure in pounds per square inch or in any other units. In the year 1643, eleven years before Guericke's public demonstration, Evangelista Torricelli, of Italy, had invented a simple instrument that was able to measure air pressure quickly and almost automatically. He called the device a *barometer*.

Torricelli was the scientific assistant and companion of Galileo in the last years of the great man's life. Galileo was then old and almost wholly blind, and one of the tasks of Torricelli, then in his thirties, was to help him with his correspondence. The idea that led to the barometer's invention came from important information in a letter Galileo received several years before his death. The letter reported that a new well dug on the plain of Tuscany was giving trouble. It had been sunk to a greater depth than was usual in that area in order to reach water. In fact, it was about 34 feet from the ground level to the water surface in the well, the usual depth being about 20 feet. An ordinary force pump had been installed, its water-pipe connection extending an additional 14 feet or so to reach the water. When the piston was moved up and down to raise the water, the pump seemed to gasp with every upstroke, but no water came out. "What is wrong?" the letter asked.

Galileo and his assistant talked the matter over. Evidently water did rise at least 20 feet in a water pipe, but it could not seem to get to a height of 34 feet, when it would have passed the first valve and then been forced out through the nozzle. Quite evidently 34 feet of water was beyond the power of the pump. But why? The problem deserved to be investigated in the laboratory.

The rest of the story belongs to Torricelli. Although he never recorded the steps that led to the barometer, they are easy to imagine. We can suppose that Torricelli thought first of setting up a 34-foot tube with a force pump at the top and a tank of water at the bottom, but such an apparatus was too large for the laboratory. If a liquid heavier than water could be used, the size of the laboratory equipment could be cut down. Mercury is approximately 13.6 times as heavy as water. Thirty inches would be about 1/13.6 of 34 feet. Instead of 34 feet of water, the pipe length for mercury would only have to be approximately 30 inches.

At this time, the glassblowers of Venice had perfected a process by which tubes of glass as much as three feet in length could be made with a central opening of an exact size throughout. Torricelli was able to get a few of them.

Deciding to substitute mercury for water, he may in the beginning have thought that a small-size force pump would be needed to raise the mercury. Then came the great idea: since he was trying to find out why the pump could raise 20 feet of water but not 34, he might start with these columns of water and study them. Or, in terms of mercury, he might start with columns of about 24 and 30 inches of mercury, and study them. A shallow trough was filled with mercury, and in the trough he placed a Venetian-glass tube about three feet long and sealed at one end. It was easy to get the air out of the tube and have mercury take its place. Now, putting a finger tightly over the open end, the tube was inserted into the trough of mercury and raised to a vertical position. When Torricelli removed his finger, the level of the mercury fell to a height of about 30 inches. The only way he could keep the mercury raised all the way to the top of the tube was to tip it sideways; when it was vertical, there was a space at the top of the column that could not be filled with air, for it completely disappeared when the tube was inclined. It must, then, be a vacuum. To make his barometer more convenient to use, Tor-

ricelli mounted it on a stand, so that the tube would always be in a vertical position.

At first he may not have been quite certain what it was that held up the 30 inches of mercury, but he was positive that the vacuum had nothing to do with it. True, many believed that a vacuum has sucking power. Yet here an outside force was pushing the mercury column up. Eventually Torricelli knew that external air pressure was holding up the column of mercury in the tube, just as it would hold up a 34-foot-high column of water, which would weigh the same as the 30 inches of mercury, in a tube of the same thickness.

Torricelli died in 1647, at the early age of thirty-nine, only four years after his invention of the barometer. At his death, many phenomena pertaining to the atmosphere and the barometer were still not understood.

How Pascal Extended the Uses of the Barometer

Blaise Pascal, of France, was a brilliant scientist, inventor, and philosopher. He was fifteen years younger than Torricelli, and, like that scientist, he died at the age of thirty-nine. Pascal heard about the barometer the year Torricelli died, and he made one for himself. After that, he kept a day-by-day record of the height of the mercury column. He wondered, as Torricelli had, about the small but slow up-and-down movements of the liquid. In a week's time the readings might vary by as much as half an inch. Sometimes the reading was higher on Wednesday and lower on Thursday and Friday, but this was not always the case. If it was low one Saturday, it might be high the next Saturday. The changes in the column's height seemed to be following a rough kind of cycle, but it had no mathematical regularity that Pascal could discover. Maybe he looked at the sky to get a clue and could find none. Perhaps the clouds there reminded him of mountains, and he wondered whether the mercury reading would be the same on a mountaintop as on the streets of Paris.

His brother-in-law, Florin Périer, lived in the French town of Clermont-Ferrand, in Auvergne, near the base of Puy-de-Dôme, a 4,800-foot mountain. Pascal wrote to him (the letter has been preserved):

> *"If it happens that the mercury is less at the top than at the bottom of the mountain . . . the weight and pressure of the air is the only cause of this suspension of the mercury . . . since it is very certain that there is much more air to weigh at the foot of the mountain than at its summit."*

Some months later the matter was checked. Périer and several companions carried a barometer to the summit of the mountain, checking it at several places on the way up. As the men climbed higher and higher, the mercury column was lower each time a reading was taken. At the peak the mercury reading was three inches less than it had been at the base. As the men descended, the mercury rose in the tube again, reaching the same reading as in the beginning when they were again at the mountain's foot. During the period of their climb, a second barometer had been set up at the bottom of the peak and was read from time to time. This unmoved instrument showed very little variation in the height of the mercury.

Pascal was now sure his idea that the mercury was held up by air pressure was correct. He made a calculation. The mercury column ordinarily was at a height very close to 30 inches. In going up a 4,800-foot mountain, the reading dropped three inches. So the atmosphere would be expected to have a height of 10 times 4,800 feet, or 48,000 feet. (His estimate was too low; air is compressible, so a larger part of the atmosphere is crowded into the first 4,800 feet, and its total height, as it spreads out, is more than 48,000 feet.)

Pascal now again began to think about the restless movements of the mercury from week to week, or even from day to day. Could the atmosphere be deeper some days than others? Or did the clouds in the sky have something to do with the situation? He began keeping elaborate records. He might watch the way the smoke went up from chimneys, or whether dew formed on the grass in the evening, or whether thundershowers occurred. Gradually he seemed to notice some sort of relationship. Low barometer readings, indicating a drop in the air pressure, seemed to come with cloudy or rainy days. High readings were associated with sunny days. A rather sudden drop seemed to foretell the coming of a fearful storm with violent winds. There was an approach to truth in his conclusions, but today's weatherman is aware that weather changes only partially follow barometer variations.

In Magdeburg, Germany, Otto von Guericke learned of Pascal's conclusion that the rise and fall of the mercury might be connected with storms, rains, and cloudless days. He wished to check this, and did so in a big way. He had a large barometer built—one whose readings could be seen half a block away after it had been set up outside his house. For the instrument he used water, not mercury; because water is so much lighter, the tube was three stories high. To make the water level easy to see, he floated a small, gaily painted wooden figure on its surface. The story goes that each day as Guericke left his home for his office, he would pause in the doorway and glance up at the top of the

barometer. If the figure was floating low, he would reenter the house and come out with his umbrella. If the figure was high in the tube he would go on, leaving the umbrella at home. He made a long study of the variations of the water's height in his barometer. Once, a sudden drop in the water level enabled him to predict the beginning of a severe storm.

Pressure Gauges for Gases

Pascal continued his study of air pressure and extended his investigations to the pressure of other gases. He developed a plan for measuring the pressure of a gas that is caught in a tight container. Pascal used an open glass U tube, which has one arm longer than the other, and some mercury. Normally there would be a barometer on the wall not far away. The U tube with the mercury could be used as a *pressure gauge*, or *manometer*, to measure how much pressure any gas being studied would put upon it.

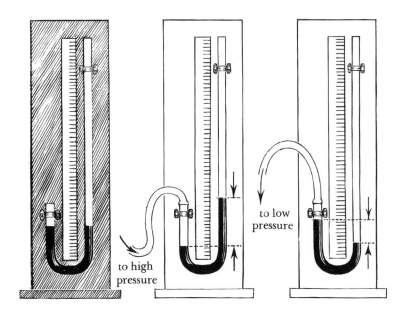

to high
pressure

to low
pressure

Before the gauge is connected to the vessel containing the gas whose pressure is to be tested, the mercury level in both arms is the same; the outside air applies the same amount of pressure to each mercury surface. After the connection is completed, by exposing one arm to the gas under study if the gas is heavier than air, the mercury rises higher in the long arm and is depressed in the other. For every 2-inch difference in the levels, the pressure of the gas in the vessel will be 1 pound per square inch more than the air pressure in the room. Air pressure averages about 14.7 pounds per square inch at sea level.

The same tube could be used to test "the completeness of a vacuum." In such a case, as the connection is completed the mercury rises higher in the short arm, being depressed in the long arm. For each 2-inch difference in the level of the mercury in the short arm over the one in the long arm, there will be a pressure of 1 pound per square inch less than the air pressure in the room. If the difference in the levels was the same as the barometer reading, the vacuum would be "complete," for there would be no air at all in the vessel.

Boyle and the Springiness of Air

In the same period that Torricelli, Pascal, and Guericke were working, a group of English scientists, meeting as a society, had been performing experiments and discussing scientific topics. Robert Boyle, who was born in 1627, was acknowledged as one of the ablest thinkers in the group, Robert Hooke as the most skillful designer of equipment.

Boyle had been experimenting with barometers, and some of his conclusions had been criticized by a Belgian professor of mathematics at the College of English Jesuits, in Liège, Franciscus Linus. Boyle felt that air both had weight and was, like a spring, capable of being compressed when pressure was put upon it and expanding when the pressure was removed. Linus said that the pressure of the air was insufficient to push mercury up to a height of 30 inches in a barometer. He thought, rather, that the mercury was held up by an extremely thin invisible substance, a "funiculus," which was at the top of the tube and attracted the mercury to itself.

Boyle defended his own findings and interpretations, claiming that there was no need to suppose such a substance. He also performed more experiments to illustrate his point about the "spring" of air. In the course of his new studies, he made a remarkable discovery.

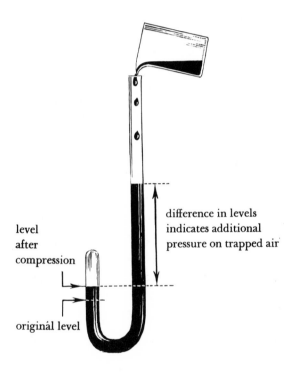

difference in levels indicates additional pressure on trapped air

level after compression

original level

This time the shorter end of a U tube was sealed, and the longer leg left open. Some mercury was then poured into this apparatus. By carefully tipping and adjusting the tube, the level of mercury was brought to the same height within both legs. The air in the shorter end was then at exactly the same pressure as the air in the room. The air in the shorter leg was compressed as the mercury rose in the next part of the experiment. With the mercury levels still equal, the volume of the air in the shorter leg was marked. Into the open end of the long leg of the tube Boyle poured mercury, which by its weight forced the liquid to a higher level in the short, sealed leg, thus compressing the air. As has been said, for every 2-inch difference in level between the two mercury levels—one inside the shorter end, the other in the longer —the pressure upon the air in the shorter leg is increased by 1 pound per square inch. Let us suppose that the difference in level reached 30 inches—a value that would have matched the reading of the mercury in another barometer in the same room. Then the pressure upon the enclosed air would be increased by 15 pounds per square inch, which means that the air in the shorter leg was under twice as much pressure as the air outside. When the volume of the air was marked and measured, it was just half of what it had been at first. Such a simple mathematical relationship!

From this point in his experiments, Boyle pursued two different ideas. One was to see whether air was perfectly springy. He tested this by removing the additional mercury that had been poured into the tube. When he had done so, the air volume went back exactly to what it had been at first. The other was to see whether a simple mathematical relationship would be found between various pressures and the matching volumes of the gas under pressure. The relationship exists: As the pressure upon an enclosed gas increases, the volume of the gas decreases at the same rate. If the pressure is decreased, the volume increases at the same rate. In other words, the volume is inversely proportional to the pressure. This is *Boyle's Law*. It holds not only for air but for gases in general.

How Cavendish Was Puzzled About Hydrogen

After Boyle's time, for about a century and a half, there was a great deal of interest in gases, and many remarkable discoveries were made. They were largely in the field of chemistry. However, the work of four outstanding scientists encompassing a period of about fifty years belongs, in part, to physics as well.

Henry Cavendish, of England, was the first to study fully and accurately that gas now known as hydrogen; in 1766 he published an account of his research. Hydrogen proved to be very light, but Cavendish had trouble calculating just what a cubic foot of it did weigh. He seems to have thought that all he would need to do to get the figure would be to fill a special bladder of soft leather with the gas and weigh it. Then he could push the bladder flat to get the gas out and weigh the empty container. The difference would be the weight of the hydrogen.

When he tried the experiment, however, something seemed wrong; the hydrogen weighed less than nothing. It and the bladder did not weigh as much as the empty bladder. He wondered if it was possible for something to have a minus weight—to fall up when released, not down. The idea did not seem reasonable. Then he realized that he had another way of checking the gas's weight. To produce the hydrogen for his original experiment, he had dissolved a piece of zinc in an acid, and hydrogen was released as a gas. Why not weigh the entire equipment—with the exception of the bladder—before the action started, and then weigh the same apparatus after the action was over? The difference should be due to the lost hydrogen, since nothing else had escaped. If that weight was negative, hydrogen weighed less than nothing. But the hydrogen did have weight, though its amount was not great. Why, then, had the filled bladder weighed less than the empty one?

Cavendish thought of Archimedes' theory that the weight of a submerged body was reduced by an amount equal to the weight of the water the body displaced. Would the idea not work for a bladder of hydrogen submerged in air? Then the negative figure he had been getting for the hydrogen was its weight diminished by that of the air it displaced. So the bladder would have "fallen upward" if the leather from which it was made were weightless, or nearly so. By replacing the bladder with an oiled-silk balloon, Cavendish found that the device did rise as he had expected.

How Dalton Developed a Theory About Gases

By the early 1780's, Cavendish added another great experimental discovery to those he had already made. He had found that exactly two volumes of hydrogen and one volume of oxygen gas unite in forming water. For this result the gases always had to be measured and combined at the same pressure and temperature. In 1808, the French chemist and physicist Joseph Louis Gay-Lussac, another skilled experimenter with gases, found that whenever two gases combined chemically, they did so in very simple ratios, so that exactly one volume of a gas would combine with exactly one, two, or at most three volumes of another. He found, for example, that two volumes of the poisonous, burnable carbon-monoxide gas react with one volume of oxygen to form two volumes of carbon dioxide, all gases being measured at the same temperature and pressure. Such simple ratios by volume were not observed with solids or liquids.

Later on, other scientists considered such relationships, as well as other facts about gases: the way they escape from opened bottles, or mix with other gases as in the air, or push back when crowded into bottles. Eventually a theory about gases was formed. John Dalton, an English scientist, was the first to clearly state this new theory. He believed that every gas was made up of tiny particles that were always in motion. These moving particles, or *atoms,* would bump into walls, producing pressure as they bounded away. Atoms of one gas bump into particles from another and rebound in different directions after the collision; thus the particles of gases would mingle together, or combine. Heated atoms moved at a faster rate than cold ones, so a gas in a closed vessel, when heated, would exert a greater pressure, which might even burst the walls. He could not check all these points by collecting these gas atoms and studying them. They were too tiny to be seen even by the most powerful of microscopes.

There were other features of these atoms that he supposed to be true, aspects that would explain what happened when hydrogen atoms and oxygen atoms united to form water particles. These suppositions Dalton included in what he called the *atomic theory,* which was the basis for many further advances in chemistry. He first proposed this theory in 1803.

In 1811, Amedeo Avogadro, of Italy, who had been following the ideas of Dalton and the gas-volume experiments of Gay-Lussac—which seemed not to agree with one another—stated that the supposed conflict of these two men's ideas could be resolved by assuming that substances are normally molecular rather than atomic. *Molecules*—larger particles composed of two or more atoms—are the particles participating in reactions when two gases combine. He assumed that equal volumes of all gases contained the same number of independent, moving molecules. Later, the word "molecules" was applied to the independent particles in liquids and solids, as well.

Blaise Pascal

CHAPTER 5

The Study of Liquids

In the last chapter, it was pointed out that because gases are so similar in behavior, a law such as Boyle's would apply to all gases. But liquids do not seem to be governed by the laws of nature in such a simple way. Water and vinegar, for example, will mix together, but water and kerosene will not. Again, water will climb up *capillary tubes*. These narrow glass containers, when dipped into water, cause the liquid to rise in them. On the other hand, mercury draws away from such capillary spaces in glass.

Yet liquids are alike in that almost all of them flow downhill. When liquids fall through the air from a dripping faucet, for example, they all form spherical drops. There is another important way in which all liquids are alike, and it was discovered by Blaise Pascal while he was still a young man.

How Pascal Found a Law for All Liquids

Perhaps Pascal found a clue to his discovery by repeating in his own way Galileo's drawings of parabolas on the garden wall. Taking an idea from Galileo's later experiments for keeping a flow of water completely steady, he fitted out a rather tall water tank with an overflow pipe and a source of water supply. In the side of the tank he put three separately controlled exits of the same size, spaced out at even distances from the water level—Galileo had used but one. Just as Galileo had done in his experiments in the garden, Pascal struck the side of the tank with a rap to flip the spurting water sideways, and marked a parabola on the wall.

Up to this point there was nothing new, nothing that Galileo had not done. But Pascal, having three exits—each producing its own form of parabola as the water spurted out—prepared a chart that would compare the three curve forms. To do this, each actual curve was moved up or down so that all started at the same location on the chart. Two horizontal lines were added, one

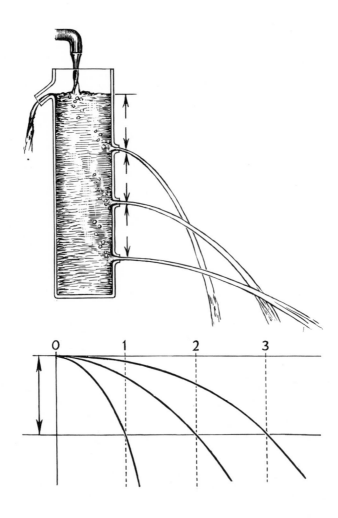

through the point at which the curves started, the second four feet farther down, indicating where the water would be at the end of a half second.

A very casual examination of the chart showed a quite simple relation among the curves. To bring it out, Pascal drew vertical dotted lines downward from the upper line, the beginning, to the three points where the curves crossed the lower line. The numbers 0, 1, 2, and 3 were placed along the top line. Measuring the spaces between these numbered points, he found them to be exactly equal. This meant that in falling for a half second, the water from the lowest opening had traveled three times as far as the water from the highest exit, and the water from the middle opening had traveled twice as far as that from the highest. Since the lowest hole was three times as far from the water level in the top of the tank, and the middle opening twice as far as the top exit, it was evident that the pressure making the water spurt out had doubled at the middle exit and tripled at the lowest. The pressure at an opening in the wall of a water tank is proportional to the depth of the opening below the water level.

Pascal was puzzled by the fact that the weight of water from the water level to an exit opening was downward but the pressure at the opening seemed to be sideways, or at a right angle with the top. He put a drop of ink into a small glass tube, carefully lowered the vial into the water, and released the drop below the surface. He could see that the ink was not lifted upward by the water below, crowded down by the fluid above, or pushed to one side or the other at its own level. It stayed where he had placed it, but gradually diffused. This meant that such a drop was under the same pressure in all directions, a fact that would be true of other drops in the liquid. A drop near an exit, before it is opened, would be under pressure from the weight of the water above, but so are all of the drops at the same level. When the exit is opened, there is nothing to keep the drop from being pushed out. If the top level of the water in the tank is held constant, keeping the weight pressure constant, other drops at the opening will be pushed out with the same pressure as the first one had been.

He was satisfied on that point, but another question came to mind. Is the pressure a result of the volume of water in the tank or of its depth? Pascal had a simple experimental way in

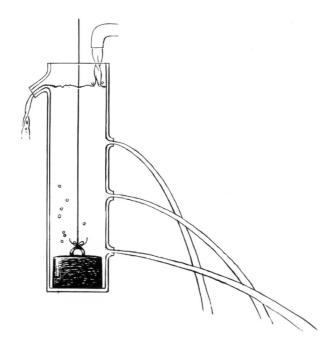

which to test the matter. A solid piece of iron was lowered into the tank he was using. The iron displaced its own volume of water, which ran out through the overflow pipe. This, of course, lessened the volume of water left in the tank. But, as he found by checking it, the pressure had not changed. It occurred to him that this conclusion would have had to be true. He remembered the old legend of the Dutch boy who saved his country from inundation by forcing his finger into a hole in the dike. The boy had been holding back the waters of the North Sea and the great Atlantic Ocean, millions upon millions of tons of liquid, with no more effort than if the dike had been along a ship canal of Rotterdam.

A Demonstration and an Invention

As Pascal's mind moved from point to point to reach general conclusions about pressures in liquids, he planned a demonstration that would in a spectacular way reveal some results of his work. He performed it in a Parisian garden, using the large house facing it as the background for his "show." The details are not known, but we can be certain of the main features. A new iron-bound oak cask had been set upon a table near the rear wall of the house. Through the side of the cask a hole had been bored, into which a special bronze stopcock had been firmly inserted. Long pieces of narrow, heavy-walled, specially blown glass tubing were connected, then run upward from the stopcock along the house wall to a balustrade two or three stories above the garden level. There, the upper end of the tubing was connected to a small funnel.

In the presence of a selected audience of notable people, the cask was filled with water, and the stopper driven in firmly. The water in the glass tubing had risen a few inches when the stopper was forced into place; this was called to the visitors' attention. A person with a vial of water appeared on the balustrade. After a few words by Pascal, the man poured the water from the small vial into the funnel. As if the cask had suddenly been filled with a furious beast fighting to escape, the lid boards swelled, and a fine spray of water hissed from the crevices. Then the stopper flew out. The terrific pressure from the inside had been produced not by a large weight of water but by the great depth of water from the level of the balustrade to the cask. Thirty-four feet of water would have brought to bear upon each square inch of interior surface a force of nearly 15 pounds.

Probably just a short time after this demonstration, Pascal announced a new law for liquids: For a confined liquid, a pressure exerted at any place on the liquid will be transmitted, unaltered, throughout the liquid, and acts at right angles to all surfaces. Thus, if the applied pressure had been 10 pounds per square inch, the pressure against every square inch of wall around the confined liquid would be increased by 10 pounds. The total force could be enormous if the vessel were big enough.

Pascal made use of the law in a practical way, creating a *hydraulic machine.* Such machines are activated by the motion of a liquid, or they move a liquid. He combined a force pump, a tank with a large hollow, easily moving piston, and a reservoir of water. The illustration shows that a pressure applied to the piston of the force pump would be passed on to every square inch of the large piston, thus raising it with a great total force. To get the large piston down again, a valve leading to the reservoir was opened to let the water out.

The basic idea behind Pascal's hydraulic machine is used today in numerous ways—for hoists, elevators, jacks, presses, and brakes. In these, other fluids are usually used. Even a barber chair is a hydraulic device.

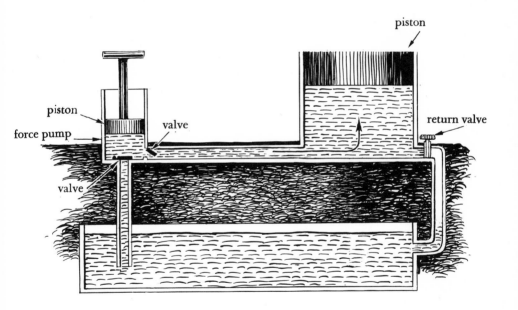

Forces at the Surface of a Liquid

The investigation of the surfaces of fluids probably began thousands of years ago. Aristotle, who was famous for his wide interests, may have been lying on a stream bank one day, watching the water bugs as they moved on the water surface without falling to the bottom of the water or getting wet. From the shadows thrown on the sandy bottom of the stream, he could tell that every foot pressed the water surface down, as if that surface were a membrane that yielded to the weight of the water bug when it moved along, but did not break through. Aristotle found such a membrane drawn across the surface of the water in a cup. It kept the liquid from overflowing even though it was higher than the brim. He probably wondered about this membrane, but could not remove it from the water. He may have taken out his knife and tried to cut away the top film that seemed to be holding the water in place in order to examine it. Instead of getting a tough, skinlike film, the water would have clung to the knife, and the cup run over.

Much later, Newton performed experiments with thin films. Such films can be made by dipping a ring of wire into soapy

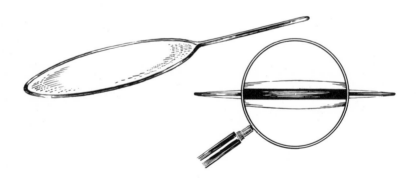

water. When the ring is drawn out, a film of liquid is stretched across it. In fact there are two films, one facing up, the other down, with a very little fluid between. The elastic force that was stretched over the surface of the stream, the cup, and the fluid in the wire is called the *surface tension* of the liquid.

Scientists after Newton's time found a way to measure how strong the surface tension of a liquid actually is. They went even further than that. Since the tension is due to the attraction of water molecules to each other, they used the value of the surface tension, and the thinness of the liquid film as it stretched across the ring of wire, to calculate the size of a molecule of water. The answer is almost unbelievably small. Across the space represented by the word "the" on this page, many millions of water molecules could be distributed.

The same force of surface tension that acts in liquid films produces spherical drops of water, drawing the liquid together into the smallest possible shape for any given volume. Larger drops become pear-shaped because of the force of gravity exerted on them.

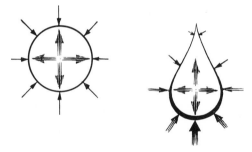

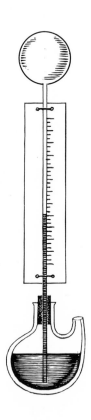

CHAPTER 6

The Measurement of Temperature

Galileo's Thermometer

As with so many other phases in the development of the science of physics, Galileo was a pioneer in the measurement of temperature, and is credited with having made the first thermometer. An early form of the instrument appears in the accompanying drawing. It consisted of a glass tube terminating in a hollow bulb. The apparatus stood in a small bottle of colored water, the bulb at the top and the tubing partially filled with the liquid. A card was attached to the tubing, with a scale marked upon it. To get water into the narrow tube, Galileo heated the glass ball gently in his hands and dipped the tube into a container of colored liquid; as the bulb cooled, the water rose high in the tube.

In using the thermometer in the sickroom, a patient's hand could be cupped around the bulb and held there for a minute or so. The warmth of his hand warmed the air within the ball, expanding it. This lowered the column of liquid. For a slightly feverish person, the fluid dropped to a lower level than it did for a normal person. The lowering was even greater for a patient with a high fever.

During the rest of the seventeenth century, many people worked on ways to improve the thermometer. One problem with the air thermometers like those Galileo had constructed was that they were subject to changes in atmospheric pressure, like barometers. The first step in improving the thermometer involved turning it upside down, with the bulb at the bottom and filled with water instead of air. Then, by about 1650, the tubes were closed at both ends, and alcohol was used instead of water. A few years later, mercury, which is what we use in most thermometers today, was employed as the liquid in the closed glass tube.

Fahrenheit Devises a Thermometer Scale

During the latter half of the seventeenth century, scientists began turning their attention to the problem of finding exactly what temperatures were indicated by the thermometric instruments. Scales were not always accurate; moreover, the instruments were of different sizes with varying proportions. Isaac Newton experimented with thermometry and devised a scale of degrees of heat ranging from the freezing point of water at the bottom to the heat of a coal fire at the top.

Gabriel Daniel Fahrenheit, who was born in 1686, was the son of a wealthy merchant of Danzig, Germany. When he was a young man, Fahrenheit left Danzig and went to Amsterdam to study. There he became interested in science, and he spent most of his life in Amsterdam and England.

As a twenty-four-year-old student, he spent the year 1708–1709 in Leyden, Holland. January of that year was unbelievably cold for that country by the sea, and during the following summer there were spells of abnormally hot weather. Everyone was complaining about the bitter cold and the suffocating heat. They would ask each other, worriedly, "Has the climate of the country changed?" "Will life in Holland ever be the same again?"

Apparently in the early fall of that student year in Leyden, young Fahrenheit asked a glassblower of the city to prepare for him a thermometer much longer than usual. The extra tubing space could be used for measuring temperatures much lower than that of a room. He decided to use alcohol in the bulb, colored red by a cloth dye.

We must do some guessing about his next moves. His scientific notebooks were probably filled with neat little numerical values and important conclusions. We know that before the fall was well under way, after much experimenting and with a glassblower's assistance, Fahrenheit constructed a liquid-holding thermometer. It had a desirable bulb size and a tube of a fine inte-

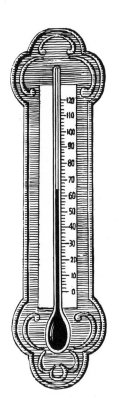

rior bore size, in order to make the rise in level noticeable even for small temperature changes. This was mounted on a piece of wood, as shown, with a scale beside the tube. Most likely the scale was close to 15 inches long, and was marked off into eighth-inch spaces, with every tenth space numbered, counting up from the bottom. This large instrument must have been ready for use before the winter began, for the daily temperatures of that fearfully cold January were recorded, as well as the temperatures of the abnormally hot summer that followed. In addition, Fahrenheit made measurements of what he called the greatest cold obtainable—a mixture of water, ice, and salt. He also measured the temperature of the blood of a healthy man. By shifting the glass parts up and down on the wooden frame, he evidently brought the temperature of the greatest cold obtainable to the zero mark on his scale. He recorded the temperature of the blood of a healthy man at 96. Each of the eighth-inch spaces was to be called a *degree*, there being 100 degrees in all. Fahrenheit liked the arrangement and kept it.

After putting so much time into his studies, he was dismayed by a sudden thought. What if the instrument he had been using for his readings was destroyed or damaged? Would not all of his recording work be wasted? Without that particular instrument, how could anyone realize how cold the zero was that year or how hot the 100 was? The matter was important—and Fahrenheit probably stopped all other work while he sought the answers.

It is possible today to follow his step-by-step accomplishments, for he reported them in scientific articles. He found that the zero temperature could be reached approximately by a freezing mixture made from two pounds of dry snow mixed with one pound of salt. Something was needed that would give the value with exactness. It finally occurred to him that any point in the lower part of the scale could be used for scale-checking if the temperature of that chosen point could be checked quickly and with high accuracy. The melting temperature of ice in a mixture of ice and water proved to be a desirable fixed point. On his scale the marking was 32.

For a second, and higher, fixed point, he seems to have tried room temperature, and also high fever. He gave them up; their positions could not be set with definite accuracy. The temperature at which pure water boils in an open vessel at Leyden was eventually chosen for the second fixed point. It was 212 on the Fahrenheit scale, as extended upward.

There were two reasons why finding the second fixed point involved more difficulties than the first. The boiling point of water is not the same the world over; it is affected by atmospheric pressure and can be much lower on a mountainside than in the valley below. There is also a slight change before a storm. Fahrenheit found these things out for himself as he went along. There was another difficulty. His alcohol thermometer, excellent for out-of-doors, would burst if placed in boiling water, since alcohol boils at a lower temperature than water. Because of this, he designed a mercury thermometer. This instrument was not an alcohol thermometer with the liquids interchanged. The liquids do not expand at the same rate.

Finally, after many months in which he had to cover the whole field of thermometry, he was ready to report his pioneering work. These reports said little about his special thermometer scale, but they gave his findings in full. The effects were immediate, and his writings were in great demand. Fahrenheit continued his scientific investigations, earning his living as a manufacturer of meteorological instruments, until his death, in 1736.

The Celsius and Centigrade Scales

In Sweden, the scientist Andreas Celsius, upon reading the report of Fahrenheit on fixed points, applied the idea to his Galilean thermometer—that is, one with the bulb at the top. He had been studying the melting points of waxes, and had extended the tubing attached to the ball so that it could be inserted in melted wax. To get the first fixed point, he simply put the bulb into melting ice; for the other, he inserted the bulb into boiling water. On this thermometer, low temperatures were at the top of the scale, high temperatures at the bottom. Celsius marked the melting of ice as 100, the boiling of water as zero (page 98).

A few years later, it was decided to turn the numbering of the scale around. The melting of ice was marked zero, the boiling of water was 100. The rearranged scale was called the *centigrade,*

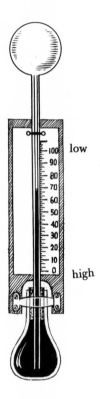

or hundred-degree, form. In a sense the name was misleading, for it implied that no other measuring system was built around the idea of 100 degrees.

As every student knows, it is easy to change the readings of either the Fahrenheit or the centigrade scales into those of the other. For example, 68° Fahrenheit is 20° centigrade. To change Fahrenheit to centigrade subtract 32 from the Fahrenheit reading and multiply by 5/9. To change centigrade to Fahrenheit, multiply the centigrade reading by 9/5 and add 32.

PART III / *The Science of Electricity and Magnetism*

Of the various powers and forces of nature, electricity seems the most mysterious. No genie of Aladdin can approach it. Throw an electric switch, and instantly—faster then you can blink an eye—lights go on. Here is a force that can be led around, harmlessly, at the end of a lamp cord. At your wish, it will operate the radio, the TV set, the phonograph, the electric clock, and a dozen other pieces of equipment.

Part III also deals with magnetism. These forces, so different from each other, are nonetheless so closely related that electricity in motion will produce magnetism, and a moving body that possesses magnetism will produce electric current.

Benjamin Franklin

CHAPTER 7

A Beginning for the Science of Electricity

No one can be given the credit for discovering electricity. The early Greeks lived in a land where thunderstorms and lightning were not uncommon. Seeing the flash of lightning and hearing the crash of thunder, they made up a story to account for these things. They thought the great god Zeus tossed thunderbolts from his home in the sky to earth when he was angry.

At some time in ancient history, the Greeks found that a stick of yellow amber, when rubbed briskly against a woolen garment, gave off tiny sparks that would set nothing on fire. The amber would also gather fine bits of light material to itself, though that power would soon be lost, and the attracted objects drop away. The Greek word for amber was *electron;* from it our word *electricity* was derived.

For two thousand years after the Greeks discovered the peculiar properties of rubbed amber, little was added to that early knowledge. By Galileo's time it was known that a sheet of paper stroked with the bare hand would produce enough electricity to cause the paper to move to a nearby wall surface and cling to it. Even the use of a dry hand in stroking a cat's fur would result in sparks and prickling shocks.

Von Guericke's Electrical Machine

Otto von Guericke helped start the science of electricity by inventing a machine which could produce electricity in a steady supply merely by turning the device's handle. We know what his machine looked like, for he described it in Book IV, Chapter 15, of his works. The long title of that chapter was "Various Virtues or Powers Exhibited by a Globe of Sulphur Which Has Been Electrified by Friction." To produce the friction mentioned in the title, he had pressed his own dry hands against a slowly revolving globe of sulphur.

He begins by telling how he prepared the sulphur globe. He placed crushed sulphur in a hollow glass sphere, as large as a child's head. The glass was warmed enough to melt the sulphur, which has a low melting point. The sulphur took the round shape of its container when it was cooled, and the glass was carefully broken away, leaving a smooth sphere of the yellow solid. Boring a hole through the center of the object he inserted an iron rod that was cemented tightly in place. A wooden base was prepared in which the mounted sphere would turn when revolved by an iron crank handle.

With his assistant turning the handle, Guericke stood next to the ball of sulphur with his dry hands gently touching it. He reported that he could soon feel the hair rising on his head, and he got a strong shock when he leaned over to touch the iron rod. Various light objects were arranged on the wooden base. After the sulphur had been stroked with his dry hand, they left the base suddenly and clung to the sphere. When it turned about on its axis, it took them with it. Next, he hung light objects at the ends of linen threads to find out how far in space the attraction would reach. In making the test Guericke touched the charged ball of sulphur with one hand and held a light metal rod in the other, reaching toward the suspended objects. They were attracted to the rod. He had expected that. Now came a kind of behavior that no one had ever reported before. Upon touching the rod, each object shot away instantly as far as the holding thread would let it go. It would go flying around at the end of its thread whenever the rod came near. When the assistant or a visitor approached the flying thing it would be attracted to the person's hand, which of course was not charged. Upon doing that, the object lost its vitality and hung quietly in the air. But any approach of the charged rod brought a repetition of the events that had taken place in the beginning. Moreover, two charged light objects were repelled from one another. He also noted that the charges, in time, leaked away from a body, whether it was a person, a rod, or a suspended object. In damp weather the loss was rapid. Guericke found a cool, dry day the best for his experiments.

The Leyden Experiment

In January, 1746, Peter van Musschenbroek, professor of physics and mathematics at the University of Leyden, was performing experiments that had been done a few months earlier by E. G. von Kleist, Dean of the Cathedral in Kamin, Pomerania. Musschenbroek, who did not know of Kleist's work, wrote to Jean

Antoine Nollet, a friend in France:"I am going to tell you about a new but terrible experiment which I advise you not to try yourself." He stated that he had been making some experiments with a new electrical machine that used a large glass globe instead of Guericke's sphere of sulphur. With this machine the globe could be spun quite rapidly, and the output of electricity was excellent if the glass was first warmed up somewhat.

The writer stated that he had suspended a gun barrel from the ceiling with silk threads, and had made a metal connection between it and the outside of the glass where the electricity would be produced when the operator held his hands on either side of the turning globe. That day, he was trying to determine what would happen to water when electrical charges were run into it. Musschenbroek hung a brass wire from the gun barrel, and passed the wire down into water in a partially filled round flask. He himself held the flask in one hand while with the other he tried to draw sparks from the electrified gun barrel. With the knuckle of his left hand, he touched the gun barrel while the right still held the flask.

> *"All at once my right hand was struck so violently that all my body was affected as if it had been struck by lightning. The flask, although made of thin glass, ordinarily does not break, and the hand is not displaced by this disturbance; but the arm and all the body are affected in a terrible way that I cannot describe: in a word, I thought it was all up with me."*

Musschenbroek told another friend that nothing in the world would tempt him to try the experiment again.

The water bottle had served as a reservoir of electrical charges, much as a dam can be a reservoir of water power. Though Musschenbroek himself did not repeat the experiment in its original form, he, his students, and other scientists were busy developing the reservoir idea into a simple but excellent electrical instrument to be called the *Leyden jar*. As shown, a heavy-walled bottle was used (since thin glass could be punctured by a heavy electrical discharge). The first jars were probably filled with salt water; later, thin sheets of metal foil coated the inside and outside walls, matching the positions where the water and hands had been. A ball-topped rod of metal, with a chain attached to it that reached the inside tinfoil, took the place of the brass wire; the ball did not permit an electrical leakage, as a sharp-pointed wire would. A plain wooden lid was used for the bottle, and the upper part of the glass, both inside and outside, was coated with heavy varnish to prevent an outside electrical-charge leakage, especially in damp weather. Soon Leyden jars became an integral part of every electrical machine.

Bold Ben Franklin

The sharp, vivid discharge of a fully charged Leyden jar resembled, on a small scale, a bolt of lightning. But no one volunteered to bring lightning into the laboratory to make a possible comparison until Benjamin Franklin, the American scientist and inventor, did so, just six years after the Leyden experiment. Franklin, born in Boston in 1706, was the first great American man of science. As a boy, he was apprenticed to an older brother who was a printer, and Franklin eventually settled in Philadelphia, where he became a newspaper publisher. He developed an interest in electricity, and for years conducted electrical experiments that he later repeated for his friends.

In 1752, Franklin carried out his famous kite experiment. It was the result of very careful thinking, for the attempt to get lightning from the clouds might be fatal if something went wrong with his plan. His table, complete with laboratory equipment that would be used to test the electricity of the lightning, was set up in a shelter, and he was assisted by a young companion.

When the experiment succeeded, scientists in Europe and America repeated it in one form or another, and no one in the scientific world doubted Franklin's conclusion that the electricity of lightning had all the properties of the electricity stored up by the Leyden jar.

In a letter to his London friend Peter Collinson, dated October 19, 1752, Franklin gave some important details of his experiment. He stated that he had made a kite from a large silk handkerchief. Fitted out with a tail and a cord of twine, the kite rose into the air like a paper kite, but it held up better against the rain and wind of a thunderstorm. He said:

> *"To the top of the upright stick of the cross is to be fixed a very sharp pointed wire, rising a foot or more above the wood. To the end of the twine, next the hand, is to be tied a silk ribbon, and where the silk and twine join, a key may be fastened."*

Silk was used because, when dry, it does not conduct electricity, and any charge that might come down the kite cord would not reach him. The key carried any electric charge to one or more Leyden jars on the table.

Franklin went on:

> *"The kite is to be raised when a thunder-gust appears to be coming on, and the person who holds the string must stand within a door or window, or under some cover, so that the silk ribbon may not be wet; and care must be taken that the twine does not touch the frame of the door or window."*

Let us try to follow the experiment by inserting into the story what Franklin did not recount to his friend. Not just any storm cloud would do. To get his kite into the cloud and yet have the storm of wind and showers come toward him, Franklin had to wait for the change of wind direction that would occur just before the shower came across the fields. Somewhere back in the distance there had to be the rumbling of thunder but no vivid stroke of lightning. Then, as the shower passed, the kite would doubtless drop to the ground. In a mere half minute or so, the experiment would be over.

As the brief shower reached the soaring kite, what could he expect? The pointed wire should gather some electricity from the cloud. The silk of the kite should become coated with a film of moisture, which would make it a mild carrier of electricity. The kite with all the twine should be electrified, and all the twine fibers should bristle out as the charge works along its dampening surface. Then, the electric charge at the key could be tested by applying a knuckle to it, just as Musschenbroek had done in his experiment. When the charge had reached the key, Franklin could charge one Leyden jar with it, then another, and another.

These things did happen. Samples of electricity from the sky were caught in the Leyden jars, and with the jar's discharge Franklin ignited an alcohol lamp and did numerous other experiments usually performed with a Leyden jar. "And thereby the

sameness of the electric matter with that of lightning [is] completely demonstrated."

Franklin's Theory of Electricity

He had demonstrated that lightning and the Leyden jar possessed the same kind of electricity. Other scientists had supposed
that there were two kinds of electricity because objects could be
given two kinds of charges. Franklin believed that there was only
one kind, and that it would be found in clouds, land, sea, and all
objects on the earth. To account for the two different charges, he
supposed that electricity could be transferred from one object to
another. When an object had more electricity than it could contain within itself, it was electrified. If one body having an excess
and another having a deficit of electricity were connected, or if a
spark passed between them, both the excess and the deficit would
disappear at the same time.

This simple explanation of what might be happening left
Franklin with one difficulty. How could he tell which of the objects had the excess of electricity? There was no way of deciding
the question by experiment. By indirect evidence he guessed that
when a glass rod was rubbed with silk, glass probably received
an excess. He marked it +, or positive. The silk was marked −,
or negative. His theory of two charges was accepted, and his
marking of + and − was to be followed universally.

The most important aspect of Franklin's theory is that it
contained a general principle known today as the *law of conservation of charge,* which Franklin proved by many different experiments. This principle stated that whenever charges appear or
disappear, they do so in equal negative and positive quantities.
Thus, when we rub a glass rod with a piece of silk, not only does
the glass become positively charged but the silk acquires an equal
negative charge. On this principle, Franklin was able to explain

the "mysteries" of the Leyden jar. If one of the conductors—say, the water or metal inside the jar—becomes charged +, the other one, the metal coating outside, becomes charged —. One conductor gains just as much charge as the other loses.

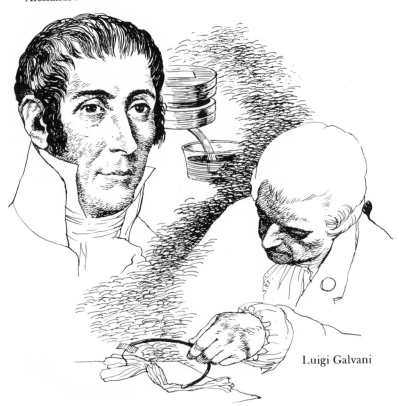

Alessandro Volta

Luigi Galvani

CHAPTER 8

Electrical Charges by Chemical Action

Galvani and the Twitching Frog Legs

In 1791, a new chapter in the science of electricity began. That year, Luigi Galvani, an Italian biologist, published an account of a series of experiments he had conducted during the preceding decade.

Galvani's investigations began after a startling event occurred in his laboratory. Like most scientists of the time, he was interested in many different areas of research. One day, he and his assistants were dissecting a frog. The moist leg was stretched out on a work table on which there also stood an electrical machine. By chance, one of the assistants took a spark from the machine at exactly the same time he touched a nerve in the frog's leg with his knife. Galvani was amazed. The animal's muscles went into mysterious convulsive movements. Somehow,

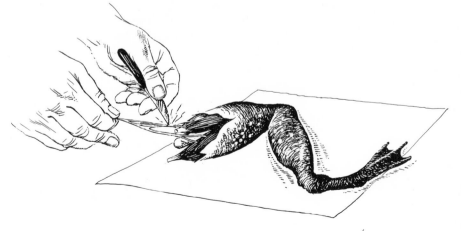

it had become part of a circuit of electrical discharge to the earth.

Other researchers had stimulated an animal's muscles, making them twitch by connecting the organ to an electrical machine or a Leyden jar. The surprising thing in Galvani's laboratory was that the frog's leg had in no way been in contact with the machine on the table. Galvani instructed one of his aides to spark the machine while he touched the nerve first with an iron rod and then with a glass rod. When glass was used, nothing happened. Clearly, electricity was involved.

The scientist wanted to find out if atmospheric electricity would produce the same effect. One day when a storm was expected, he took a group of legs from recently dissected frogs attached to brass hooks and hung them outside his laboratory on an iron trellis. He waited. When the storm came, the result was just what he had anticipated. Every time there was a flash of lightning overhead, the strange twitches occurred.

Again, chance played a part in Galvani's work. He continued his outdoor experiments, and one day when the weather was fine, he happened to press the brass hook from which a freshly prepared specimen was hanging against the iron lattice. This time there was no electric machine, no lightning, but the mysterious convulsive movements occurred anyway. This was an entirely new electrical phenomenon.

Galvani tried to understand where the electricity had come from. He decided that the frog's leg still had a supply of "vital" electrical energy possessed by the living animal. This electricity, he believed, flowed from the brain through nerves to the muscles. A muscle, then, like a Leyden jar, had one electrical charge on its surface and the opposite one in its interior. When he published his report, scientists and others hearing of his work were excited by the results of the experiments, the theory, and the possible relation of electricity to life.

During the course of his research, Galvani discovered another startling fact. He wrote:

> *"We were fortunate enough to observe this peculiar and remarkable phenomenon, that the use of more than one metallic substance and the differences between them contribute much to the excitation . . . also especially to the increase of the muscular contraction, far more indeed than when one and the same metal is used."*

Thus, if he stretched the leg out on an iron plate and touched it with an iron rod, either the contractions did not occur at all or they were very small. But if, for example, one of the objects was iron and one brass—it did not matter which—a strong response resulted. Either the electricity was in the animal or it was the result of the junction of two metals. Galvani insisted that his theory of animal electricity was right. By the time he died, in 1798, it had been shown that he was wrong, and this great discoverer had become a disappointed and bitter man.

Volta Studies the New Way of Producing Electricity

One of the scientists interested in Galvani's report was Alessandro Volta, a professor of physics at the University of Pavia, about twenty miles south of Milan. Only a few years younger than Galvani, he was an expert in the field of electricity and had invented a *condensing electroscope.* This instrument indicated the presence or absence of an electrical charge. Volta's device was far more reliable than earlier types. It was so sensitive that it could detect electrical charges in water vapor and in the smoke from burning coals.

Excited by Galvani's report, Volta repeated many of the experiments. As he continued to work, his doubts about Galvani's theory increased, and he became convinced that the electrical charge was due to the metals, and did not come from the animal itself.

By 1792, he had extended his experiments to the muscle and the body fluid surrounding it. Trying to see which of these was of greater importance, he soaked a piece of cloth with body fluid, and, omitting the muscle, he touched the cloth at two separate places with strips of zinc and copper. Volta watched his electroscope carefully. Every time the metals came in contact with the moist cloth, the device indicated the presence of a charge, and just as great a charge as had occurred with the moist muscle. The frog's leg, then, was not important to charge formation; like the electroscope, it had merely indicated, by twitching, that a charge was produced.

But could two strips of different metal conduct a current through other moist substances? Paper, leather, and cloth soaked in water or other liquids were substituted in the experiment. Always, when the zinc and copper came in contact with the moist substance, a charge was produced.

The Voltaic Pile

Volta's experiments had shown him that, even without a Leyden jar or other source of electricity, some metals received a positive charge and some a negative one when they came in contact with each other. Moreover, the strength of the charge differed. Zinc seemed to have the strongest positive charge, copper and silver the strongest negative one.

In 1796, he devised his first *voltaic pile*. It was a simple arrangement of pairs of discs—one zinc and one silver—in contact with one another and separated from the next pair by a piece of leather or pasteboard soaked in water or some other fluid. This remarkable invention seemed to produce an almost unending flow of electric current. Unlike the Leyden jar, it did not have

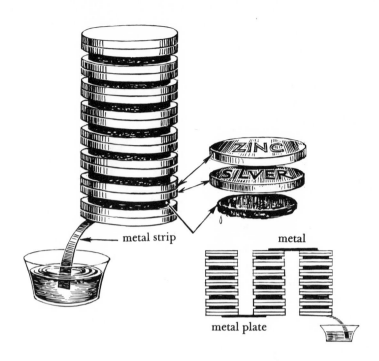

metal strip   metal

metal plate

to be recharged after each burst of electricity. Nor did it have to be charged in advance by means of an outside source.

Just as two diesel engines have twice the pulling strength of one when the engines are attached, one behind the other, to a train, so the quantity of electricity produced by the pile could be increased by having several columns attached to one another. This was done by means of terminal plates at the top and bottom of a stack of the paired discs. As the drawing shows, these metal plates were stretched across from the center of one column to the center of the next, and were alternately placed at the tops and bottoms of the pairs of piles.

One problem with the pile was that as the moist pieces of leather or cardboard dried out, the current weakened. To prevent this, Volta designed what he called his "crown of cups." It consisted of a series of jars partially filled with water mixed with salt or lye. Adjoining cups were connected to each other by an arc of copper or brass wire. At one end of the arc was a strip of zinc, and at the other a strip of copper or silver. The cups were arranged in a circle; thus, each one had a plate of zinc and one of silver, and was connected to both its neighbor containers.

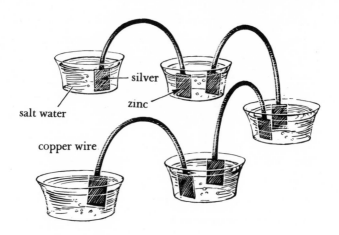

Volta's invention, the forerunner of the batteries we use today, opened up a whole new era in science. It marked the start of the field known as *electrochemistry,* and was the basis of all later practical applications of electricity. By the time this great scientist died in 1827, at the age of 82, he could take satisfaction in the rapid advances his discoveries had made possible.

Chemical Action in the Voltaic Cell

A diesel engine requires fuel to operate; so does the voltaic cell. It gets its energy supply from chemical action. A simple modern cell could be made from two strips of dissimilar metals like zinc and copper, called the *electrodes,* which are immersed in a fluid, the *electrolyte.* Today, dilute sulphuric acid would be used instead of the liquids of Volta's early experiments.

In order to understand the chemical action that takes place, it is necessary to know something about the very small particles that all matter is composed of. *Atoms* are the smallest particles into which an *element,* such as copper or zinc, can be divided and still retain its physical properties. *Compounds* are chemical unions of two or more elements; sulphuric acid is a compound made up of hydrogen, oxygen, and sulphur. Atoms contain a number of smaller particles. Among them are *electrons,* which are negatively charged, *protons,* which are positively charged, and *neutrons,* which are neutral in charge. An *ion* is an atom or group of atoms that has become electrically charged by gaining or losing charged particles.

When sulphuric acid is put into solution and diluted, it breaks up into two kinds of ions, which move freely through the liquid. One kind, linked hydrogen and oxygen atoms, is positively charged; the other ions, sulphur and oxygen atoms linked together, are negatively charged. As the zinc and copper strips are connected by a wire, action occurs at both electrodes. Zinc atoms go into solution as positively charged zinc ions, each atom leaving two electrons behind it. These are negatively charged and repel one another, moving up the wire to the copper.

At the same time, the positively charged zinc ions repel the hydrogen ions, which have the same charge, and the hydrogen tends to move toward the copper, where it can pick up electrons and thus become neutral. The copper, of course, continues to gain electrons traveling from the zinc along the wire. This flow is an *electric current.*

A voltaic cell continues to transform chemical energy into electrical energy until the zinc or the hydrogen ions are used up. The copper is not affected in this way and does not have to be replenished. Thus, for practical use, the zinc is normally purchased as a thick block, the copper as a thin, wide strip of metal. In the chemical action, the zinc ions are not destroyed. They change their location, however, and end up, along with the sulphur-oxygen ions, as a new compound, zinc sulphate, which remains in the fluid.

The Discovery of the Electron

When Volta invented his battery, and for a long time afterwards, the nature of an electric current was not understood. In fact, during the early years of the nineteenth century scientists were uncertain whether the frictional, or static, electricity produced by the Leyden jar and voltaic electricity, the electric current produced by the battery, were two different forces or varying aspects of the same force. The frictional type seemed uncontrollable, like some furious, untamed wild steed of the hills. The other could be likened to the workhorse of a prairie farm.

In 1833, the Englishman Michael Faraday, whose experimental work on electricity and magnetism was of enormous scope, delivered a paper to the Royal Society of England on the "identity of electricities." In it, citing numerous experiments of his own and reviewing current knowledge of the subject, Faraday proved that the electricity produced by machines was the same as that produced by batteries. In the case of the machine, the quantity of electricity produced was low. The pressure behind it was extremely high. Electricity from the battery was larger in quantity, but the pressure behind it was quite low. However, Faraday left unanswered the question "What is it that races along the wire when the proper connections are made?" Nonetheless, he did make a start toward a solution.

In 1838, he published an account of some observations he had made while studying the discharge from an electric machine. The burst of electricity looked like a small lightning stroke. Were the zigzag motions due to the molecules of the air getting in the way of the electrical discharge? To check on that possibility, he took a closed glass tube that had metal terminals at either end and was connected to an air pump. Faraday connected the tube to the machine, and passed the electrical discharge across the space from one terminal to the other inside the tube. The zigzag streak of light appeared as before. Then he pumped some of the air out and watched the result. When most of the air was gone, a violet-colored thread of light seemed to extend from one electrode to the other. Around the negative terminal, which he had named the *cathode,* a tuft of light appeared. When he had expelled as much air as the air pumps of that day were capable of removing, there was a glow around each terminal and a dark space in between. For lack of a better air pump, he could go no further.

In 1855, Heinrich Geissler, a skilled glassblower and mechanic, invented a new kind of vacuum pump that enabled scientists to get a much more complete vacuum in their tubes. Within a few years it was known that a more complete removal of the air in Faraday's tube made the glow disappear. But the glass around the *anode*—the positive electrode—glowed with a bright-green fluorescent light. Between the fluorescence and the cathode nothing could be seen, but something invisible was moving between the two electrodes.

Two experiments yielded a clue to what this was. In the first, developed by the English chemist Sir William Crookes, a solid object shaped like a cross was put in the tube, attached to the anode and in front of the cathode. When the electrical discharge traveled through the tube, a well-defined shadow of the cross could be seen on the glass opposite the cathode. This certainly suggested that something was traveling in a straight-line path across the tube. In the second experiment, described by Crookes in 1879, when a green fluorescent glow appeared in the tube, a strong magnet was placed at its side. When the positive pole of the magnet was next to the glass, the spot of glowing light was diverted toward it. Upon reversing the magnet, the spot moved away, repelled by the negative pole. With a stronger magnet, the location of the glowing spot was diverted farther than before. Apparently the "something" moving away from the cathode was a tiny particle carrying a negative charge. It was not, however, of atomic or molecular size, and nothing smaller than a hydrogen atom had ever been imagined at that time.

In 1891, Dr. G. Johnstone Stoney suggested the name *electron* for such a particle. Many scientists continued to investigate the nature of the electron, and then, in 1897, Sir J. J. Thomson, in a decisive experiment, proved the existence of the electron and determined its properites. He found that the electron was a negatively charged particle, and later that its mass was approximately 1/1,800 as heavy as a hydrogen atom.

With the knowledge that there was such a very tiny particle associated with it, many of the puzzling points about electricity could be explained. Franklin's "excess of electricity" could now be interpreted as an accumulation of electrons. The "flowing of electricity through a wire" represented the rapid motion of electrons as they are repelled from behind and attracted by positive charges ahead. But the relation of the electron to the atom was not known then, nor was it understood how the zinc of the voltaic cell, as it was acted upon chemically, could play a part in producing electrons for the flow of electric current. Such explanations were not forthcoming until the twentieth century.

Michael Faraday

Thomas Alva Edison

CHAPTER 9

Magnetism and Electricity

Certain things about magnets and magnetism seem very strange. For example, if there were only one magnet in the whole world, that single piece of metal would be able to magnetize the steel needles on all the compasses of the earth, and it could do this without losing its own magnetic power. Again, a force like gravitation affects all objects on our planet; magnetism appears to affect only iron, steel, and a few other substances.

The Lodestone and the Compass.

About three thousand years ago, it was accidentally discovered that pieces of a certain grayish-black mineral—*lodestone,* called *magnetite* today—would cling to the iron point of a spear. This mineral is a compound of iron and oxygen, and it is a natural magnet. The Greeks noted that not only did a lodestone cling to an iron spearhead, but the iron head of the spear was just as strongly attracted to the lodestone. Many centuries later, Newton stated that this action was in accord with the Third Law of Motion. Only one force was at work; it was acting equally and oppositely upon the rock and the iron spearhead.

At some early time it was discovered that the power of magnetism possessed by a lodestone could be passed on to an iron knife merely by stroking its blade with the stone. The lodestone would be drawn down the full length of the blade, then lifted and returned through the air to its starting point. Many strokes were needed to make a good magnet.

Then some experimenter must have noticed that when a piece of magnetized iron was free to turn in a horizontal plane, it always assumed a position in which one end faced north and the other south. This discovery, which was made in China nearly three thousand years ago, was very important in the history of magnetism and magnets. But it was the navigators of the Western world who first put the compass to practical use. They used steel, which is an alloy of iron and carbon, as the magnetized metal, mounting it on a small block of wood floating in water. The steel needle, and the wood block with it, was free to turn in any direction as it floated on the water. Always, it adjusted its direction so that one end pointed toward the Pole Star; the other end, of course, faced south. If the position of the block was changed, it was but a short time before the needle again faced north-south. It would do this all day long and at night, too, whether the Pole Star could be seen in the sky or not.

It would not have been long before some sea captain took such an arrangement with him when he went to sea. This was the world's first *compass*. A sea captain would also take along a lodestone with which the steel bar would be stroked occasionally to maintain its magnetism. Our present-day magnetic compass is different in that it has a bar of thin steel that turns freely on the tip of a pivotal point. It was one of the greatest experimenters in the field of magnetism, the English scientist William Gilbert, who developed the theory that the earth itself was a giant magnet. In 1600 he published a volume containing all the verifiable information about magnetism known at the time. Gilbert also was the first person to make a drawing of the lines of force around a magnet.

More than three hundred years later, in the year 1820, a momentous discovery was made about electricity and magnetism. This discovery was, within eighty years, to change the commercial applications of electricity to such a vast extent that one might call the last part of the nineteenth century the Era of Electricity. Some of the men of pure physics who worked out the basic principles and the men of applied physics who designed the instruments and commercial equipment for the Era of Electricity are described below.

Oersted's Discovery

The spring of 1820 was moving on toward summer. In the Danish University of Copenhagen, Professor Hans Christian Oersted, an inspiring teacher, was nearing the end of a lecture in his course on magnetism, machine electricity, and voltaic electricity. The course had been illustrated by numerous lecture experiments. On this day, the instruments and devices that had been used were on movable tables or stands at the sides of the lecture platform. On one table were the magnets and compasses used in the lectures on magnetism. On another, Oersted had an electric machine, Leyden jars, and pith balls on threads hanging from supports. On a third table stood a large voltaic battery; next to it was a copper wire several feet long that could be fastened almost instantly over the battery terminals.

The topic being discussed that day was, apparently, a comparison of the forces of magnetism and electricity. In that lecture, Oersted might have mentioned that gravity attracts; it has no other action. Magnetism and electricity, as forces, can attract or repel. For a magnet, the poles are marked north and south.

The terminals of a battery are similar to these magnetic poles; they are marked positive and negative. Indeed, the two terminals might be called poles. In both the battery and the magnet, the poles are equally strong. Unlike poles attract; like poles repel. There is, however, one marked difference between magnetism and electricity in connection with the poles. In magnetism, no pole can be moved off by itself. If a magnet is broken apart in an attempt to move the north pole away, the large magnet merely becomes two magnets, as new south and north poles form at the break. But the positive and negative charges in electricity, though formed at the same place, can be moved as far apart as desired.

There seems to be a similarity between the powers of magnetism and electricity, Oersted may have gone on to say. But magnetism exerts its powers only upon iron, steel, and a few other substances. Electricity is not selective in this way, though it is true that charged particles race or drift through metals and are generally stopped by nonmetallic substances. Up to Oersted's time, no one had ever shown that there is even the slightest direct relation between these two powers.

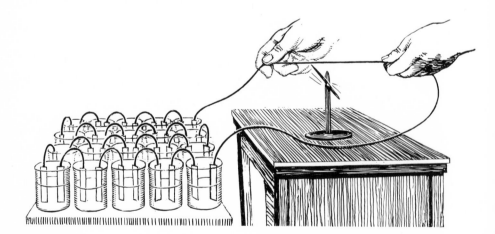

At the end of his lecture, Oersted set a compass on his desk. Then he drew the table holding the voltaic battery, which had been used during the lecture, toward him. He picked up the copper wire, connected it to the battery terminals, and lowered the wire toward the compass needle. As the current-carrying wire descended, the needle suddenly seemed to be trying to twist out from under it. Oersted was perplexed by the result of this experiment. He reversed the flow of the current, and the needle swung in the opposite direction. Whatever Oersted did with the wire, the needle reacted to it. There was obviously some relation between the electric current and the magnetism of the compass. The students crowded near the lecture desk.

Oersted wrote to all of his scientific friends, telling them of his great discovery. Then he published a report about his experiments. Soon all the scientists of Europe and America had heard the news, and many were busily experimenting with it.

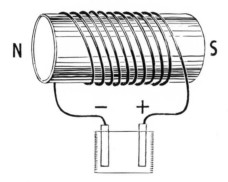

Solenoids and Electromagnets

The *solenoid* was the first electrical device to be developed from the newly discovered relation of magnetism and electricity. It consisted of a coil of wire that could be connected to a battery.

During the same year that Oersted published his report, the French physicist André Marie Ampère experimented with a solenoid. He found that when the current was turned on, the device behaved like a magnet. If the coil were wound like a right-handed screw, the north pole would be at the end where the current leaves the wire. By reversing the direction of the current, the magnetic poles were also reversed. Ampère developed a theory, still regarded as essentially correct, that the magnetic phenomenon was not a totally separate thing, but in fact just one of the effects of electric currents.

The solenoid was only a weak magnet, but it was the forerunner of the most useful application of the magnetic properties of electric currents, the *electromagnet.* Usually, this is a coil of wire wound spirally back and forth in a number of layers around a core of soft iron. When the wire is connected to a battery or another source of electricity and the current is turned on, an electromagnet behaves just like, and can be made much stronger than, any permanent magnet.

The first electromagnet was made in 1823 by the English scientist and inventor William Sturgeon. His device was made up of a single layer of bare wire wound around an iron core that was insulated from the wire by a wax coating. It could support weights of up to nine pounds.

Four years later, the noted American physicist Joseph Henry made a small but very important modification of the electromagnet. It was he who first insulated the wire wound around the core, and he used many layers of wire instead of only one. By 1831, Henry had built a magnet that could support 750 pounds.

Signaling with Electricity

Joseph Henry did not concentrate on large magnets only; he also constructed small electromagnets that could be attached to the battery with long lines and operate at a great distance from the power source. By 1831 he had constructed an elementary telegraph that operated through a mile of wire.

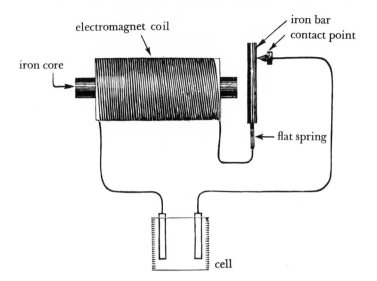

electromagnet coil

iron core

iron bar
contact point

flat spring

cell

Scientists experimented with many different ways to use electromagnets as signaling devices. One of the early kinds is shown in the illustration. A soft iron bar held by a flat spring opposite the end of the electromagnetic coil is pulled toward the coil as the current flows. At the rear of the iron is a contact point across which the electricity passes on its way from battery to electromagnet and back to the battery. As the magnetic action pulls on the iron, the bar moves away from the contact point, and the current stops. The iron is no longer attracted to the electromagnet, and it is released. The elasticity of the spring brings the bar back toward the contact point. As the iron touches the point again, the current starts. So, back and forth the spring-held iron will go. When the iron acts as a clapper, striking a bell as it moves, the device can operate as a bell. About a century and a quarter ago it must have been a fascinating experience to watch the pressing of a key cause bells to ring and guns to go off.

The Morse Telegraph

In the year 1844, Samuel F. B. Morse, an American artist and inventor, succeeded in transmitting the first message by way of his great invention, the telegraph, which had been anticipated by Joseph Henry. The idea for the telegraph had come to Morse in 1832, and the first model was constructed in 1835. Then it took him ten years to get financial backing for the first telegraph line. Here is the way the invention was described in the patent application:

> *"This [electromagnetic apparatus] is composed of a wire or line which forms an electric circuit; a battery or electricity generating system mechanism for transmitting current over the wire; a key, transmitter or needle for making and breaking the current; and a receiving apparatus which records the makings and breakings of the current by a sounder, or pointer, or markings on a moving tape."*

Besides the apparatus, Morse invented a telegraphic code to use with it. The code, as everyone knows, consists of combinations of dots and dashes representing the letters of the alphabet, numbers, and other characters.

A special type of telegraph battery had to be used. The current it would deliver had to be instantly available at all times; when flowing, the current had to be completely steady in quantity, and all needed replacement of parts had to be so easy to do that every station operator could handle the matter for himself. To keep costs down, the current going over the miles of wire between stations was not great in quantity. As a result, the clicking sounds heard at the receiver were rather faint and could be drowned out by the noise of passing steam locomotives or the clattering of train cars. Because of this, Morse developed a special plan. He fitted a local electrical circuit to the faint main-line receiver. The local circuit had its own battery, its own specially designed resonant sounder, whose clear, bold sounds would rise above railroad noises, but it had no hand-operated key. Its key was the chattering sound bar, or *armature,* of the main-line receiver,

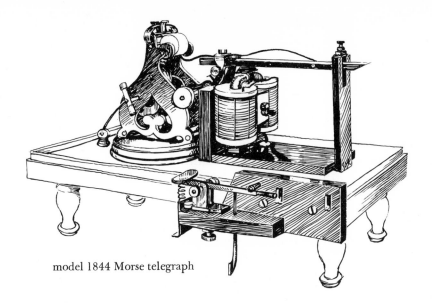

model 1844 Morse telegraph

which Morse called a *relay*. Though the relay gave sound signals that were faint at its sound bar, the bar, by touching the contact point, would release the strong local current. Thus, for every electric pulse that made the dots and dashes, two sounds were merged together—one the weak noise of the relay, the other the strong noise of the local sounder.

The first telegraph line of 1844 went only from Baltimore to Washington. But twenty-five years later such lines had crisscrossed the country. Messages traveled with almost the speed of light, millions of times faster than the Pony Express riders had ever raced.

The Electric Motor

The story of the applications of electricity continues with the development of the electric motor. On Christmas morning in 1821, Michael Faraday dashed from his laboratory to the kitchen, where his wife was roasting the Christmas goose. We can imagine his excitement. "Sarah, the motor is running smoothly. Come on and see it!" "Well, just for a moment." And she went with him to his laboratory to see the first magneto electric motor. It was operated by a single battery cell, and a magnet was caused to rotate around a wire carrying an electric current. We might think of it as having the strength of one "mousepower." No electromagnet was part of the mechanism, so it was not at all like the later motors. Yet the machine ran smoothly and could be reversed in its motion quite readily. This was but a year and a half after Oersted's discovery, and the knowledge of electromagnetism was just getting under way.

The motor with an electromagnet as a moving part was soon invented, but early forms did not operate with a smooth motion. This can be shown in the sketch of a simple motor. The upright axis is a slender stick of wood. The coil of wire is wound around a small tube of cardboard, and pieces of soft iron baling wire are put into the cylinder. The two ends of the wire are bare, and are wrapped around the wooden upright. Flat spring-metal strips, touching these wire ends, are connected to a one-cell battery. Two permanent magnets are placed as shown. The battery contacts are made with a wire held in each hand. To reverse the current in the electromagnet, the hand connections at the battery are reversed.

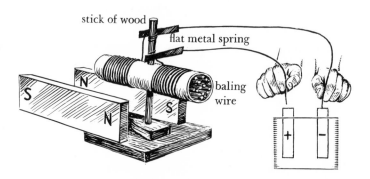

The operation of this motor is simple. When the current flows and the electromagnet is in the pictured position, it is magnetized with a north pole at one end and a south pole at the other. If the electromagnet's poles are at the same ends as those of the permanent magnets, the poles would repel one another, and the electromagnet would turn away from the permanent magnets. After turning a half revolution, the motor would stop with a jerk unless battery connections were quickly reversed, thus reversing the electromagnet poles; another half revolution would follow. If the connections are reversed at the proper time, the motor can keep on turning.

Today's commercial motors handle the reversing of connections mechanically, not at the battery or electrical source but at the turning electromagnet itself. For smoothness of pull, the electromagnet is divided into many separate ones whose changing poles follow each other to give a steady over-all pull. The two permanent magnets of the simple model are replaced by a larger number of separate, unmoving electromagnets.

Advances by Faraday

Some ten years later, in August of 1831, another idea occurred to Faraday. Perhaps he was out under the trees in the garden, lazily watching the sky. All his experimental projects had been finished, the reports written. He had not made up his mind about next year's program.

Before the lazy day was over, Faraday remembered some notes he had made in 1822. If electricity can be used to produce magnetism, why should magnetism not be able to produce electricity? This same idea had occurred to Joseph Henry. In 1831, Faraday got a hint that electricity could be produced from magnetism. During a total of ten years of further experimentation and thinking, that hint was broadened and enlarged to become the basis for the telephone, electric lighting, and electric-power developments that came about in the next half century.

Faraday's London laboratory, in the famed Royal Institute on Albemarle Street, was large and well equipped. Before the ten-year period of experimentation was over, a host of new pieces of equipment had been designed and constructed. But in the beginning of the new research program only existing devices were used. They had been developed in connection with the production of magnetism by electricity. Now they were to be useful in the attempt to produce electricity by means of magnetism.

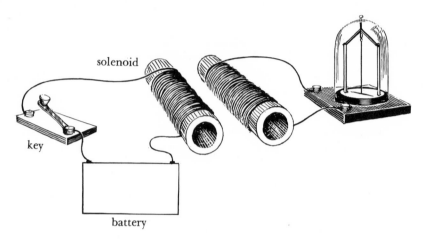

A few of the early experiments, using existing equipment, will be described. In the first, two adjacent but completely separate circuits were laid out. The left-hand one was composed of a solenoid on a hollow wooden cylinder, a battery, and a key. The other used a similar solenoid in circuit with a *galvanometer*. This instrument had a needle that moved upon a dial, the needle being held at the zero position by a lightweight coiled spring; it could move in either direction, and so was used to measure both the direction and the intensity of a current. Faraday had used this instrument in earlier experiments. With the two solenoids near each other, he pressed the key. There seemed to be a slight fluttering of the needle, but it was gone almost instantly. For the half minute or so that the current remained on, the needle was completely still. When the key was released, there was again a slight motion, then complete calm.

In the next experiment, the previous equipment was used,

but with this change: Pieces of soft iron wire were pushed through the hollow solenoid centers and fastened to the solenoid wires to make a metal ring. Faraday may also have added an additional cell to his battery. Pressing the key gently, watching intently to see what would happen, he was startled by the action. The galvanometer needle flew completely around the dial five or six

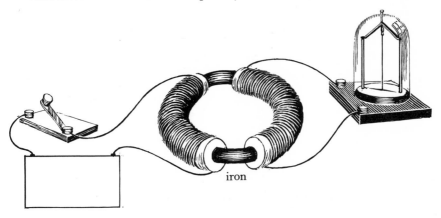

iron

times, then quickly returned to the starting position, although the key had been pressed for the full time, so there had been a constant flow of current. When the key was released, the needle moved around again in a direction opposite to its first spin.

In making the report that went into his laboratory journal, Faraday called the circuit that included the galvanometer the *secondary circuit,* and the current formed the *induced current.* By contrast, the battery circuit was referred to as the *primary circuit;* its current was the *inducing current.*

He wrote: "An electric current is induced in the secondary circuit at the instant that the key is closed in the primary circuit: the directions of the currents are opposite. A current is also induced when the key is released. Its direction is opposite to the previous induced current. There is no induction while the current is flowing steadily in the primary circuit."

The action seemed to be due to magnetism, and not to the

current flowing in the primary circuit. The matter could be checked by using a permanent magnet instead of the electro-magnet of the second experiment. Faraday retained the solenoid and galvanometer arrangement. Then, grasping a bar magnet in his hand, its north pole down, he thrust the magnet into the solenoid opening. The needle moved while the magnet was in motion, and returned to its original position when the magnet was stationary. When the magnet was withdrawn quickly, the needle moved, but in the opposite direction. If the magnet were turned around, and the south pole thrust into the solenoid and then pulled out, the needle's motion was as before, but in the opposite direction.

bar magnet

These were but the first of an enormous number of ex-periments made by Faraday that were related to induced cur-rents. In the course of this work he devised a piece of equip-ment that could produce a steady flow of electricity as one turned its handle; he called it a *generator*. In later years, genera-tors would, in large part, take the place of batteries for the production of electricity.

Bell and the Telephone

Alexander Graham Bell and Thomas Alva Edison were born in the same year, 1847. They were twenty-one when Faraday retired, in 1868. Each of them was affected greatly by Faraday's discoveries in the field of electromagnetism. Bell was born in Scotland and came to Boston, where he settled, by way of Canada. In Boston, he became a noted teacher of speech and elocution, working especially with the deaf. Being scientifically inclined, he was fascinated by the nature of sound vibrations as produced by the mouth and throat and received by the ear. From this interest, the idea for the telephone grew. Edison was to develop a similar interest in sound vibrations into his inventions of the dictating machine and the phonograph.

Had Bell been content to produce an arrangement that carried a message by electricity a mere mile or less, he could have used a rather simple, three-step arrangement. First, he might have introduced at the mouthpiece a soft-iron diaphragm that would move back and forth in time with the sound vibrations reaching it. The moving diaphragm then would act on a package of carbon grains, which was developed by Edison, exerting varying amounts of pressure and then releasing it. By varying the compactness of the grains, their electrical resistance is varied. When the granules are compressed, they are in good contact with one another, and offer less resistance to the flow of electrical current than when they are released. An electric current passing through the granules would then fluctuate as the sounds are produced. As the third step, the current variation, moving over the wire and applied through an electromagnet, affects a soft-iron diaphragm at the receiver on the far end of the line, its movement being a series of vibrations approximately similar to those of the mouthpiece diaphragm. This vibration would send sound waves into the air.

To get an instrument that was satisfactory for a longer distance, some way had to be found to strengthen the current, which had been weakened by the resistance of the wires it passed through for long distances. Two circuits were linked through electromagnets. The number of turns of wire making up the primary coil were few, those of the secondary coil were many. The result was a *step-up induction coil,* the induced current flowing through its circuit at much higher pressure than the original current. So, a telephone current that would be so weak as to be inaudible could be stepped up and emerge with as great energy as at the source, or even greater.

The sketch shows a telephone of 1882; the following quotation refers to the telephones of those days:

> *"You shouted into the mouthpiece to make yourself heard, and you shushed the family so you in turn could hear. And the sounds of the voice were so distorted that you could not be sure who was answering, though you could distinguish a woman's voice better than a man's."*

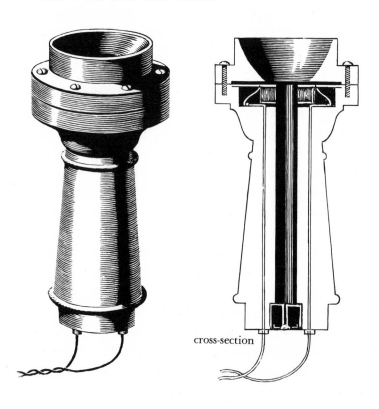

cross-section

Young Edison

Thomas Alva Edison said that he grew up with telegraphy. He was born three years after the first telegraph line was stretched from Baltimore to Washington. At fourteen he would stand for hours watching telegraph operators at work and listening to the clicking of the sounders as messages went through. At sixteen he has passed the tests to be a telegrapher, and then wandered through the Midwest working at one small railroad station after another. At first the time passed swiftly as he practiced sending the Morse code. Books on electricity were at that time difficult to get, but he was filled with excitement when he found a new one.

Edison, being restless and inventive, began making various simple electrical contrivances. His first important one was called an "automatic telegraph repeater." This contrivance brought him some publicity, but also got him fired from his first job as a telegraph operator. This is the story that was told after he became famous: Most of the night-shift telegraphers on the same section of the railroad line were young men. There were periods when almost no messages were sent or received, and then the young men would indulge in some horseplay over the wires. Although sixteen-year-old Tom Edison did not start this tomfoolery, he went along with the crowd. One day Tom set out to hoodwink the others by preparing a mechanical arrangement, much like a music box, that would press dots and dashes as it turned. He had the "box" arranged to give his code call, to be followed by "OK Edison." Then it gave the sign-off signal.

The day he was caught, he had added something to the automatic repeater. His alarm clock was wired so that the minute hand, as it completed a revolution every hour, would turn on the repeater at some set time. It is unclear how he expected to use the arrangement, but he had been testing it. Falling asleep in his chair, he unintentionally left the clock connected. That night the supervisor, trying to reach Tom over the line, got no answer. He assumed that the lad had left the station for a few moments. But while he waited the automatic device suddenly cut in, gave its message, and signed off. Yet the supervisor, after trying repeatedly, got no answer to his calls. He reported later that he was afraid a bandit had slipped into the telegraph booth, forcing Tom to send his message but not letting him answer any incoming calls. Hastily borrowing a railroad handcar, and picking up an armed companion, the supervisor hurried to Tom's station. No operator could be seen, but suddenly, in dots and dashes, the automatic sender gave its "OK Edison." Tom was asleep again, but in the back room. The automatic telegraph repeater was smashed.

Young Edison lost his job, but he got a better one almost immediately, and his idea for the contrivance went with him. Modified, it appeared as a stock ticker-tape recorder. He sold a group of ticker-tape patents for $40,000 and invested the sum in a building, equipment, and machinery. His career as an inventor was under way.

The Edison Incandescent Light

Edison was the inventor of a number of outstanding contrivances. One of the most important was the carbon-filament incandescent light. At that time, kerosene lamps were used for home lighting. For factories in the larger cities and for street lights, a gas manufactured from coal was used. Edison believed that electricity could serve these purposes, and do them safely and well.

A fine iron wire can be heated white hot by an electric current. If the air can be pumped out of a container in which the wire is kept, the iron does not burn up. But to supply a satisfactory amount of light, the wire would have to be heated so much that it would melt and fall apart. Edison tested a number of metals with high melting points. None was satisfactory as a source of incandescent lighting, but the two that came closest were tantalum and tungsten. Unfortunately, both were extremely difficult to draw out as fine filaments of wire, and when the filaments were formed, they were so brittle that they could not be touched without breaking. By the first decade of the twentieth century, these problems had been solved and tungsten-filament lamps were produced.

By 1879, Edison had developed, first, fibers of carbonized cotton thread and, afterward, strong filaments of carbon from charred bamboo fibers, which emitted a soft yellowish-white light. But a satisfactory plan for lighting houses, factories, and streets required much more than this. First came the construction of the lamp bulb that would house the filament. It must allow the electric current to enter and leave the inner space, from which the air was removed, by wires that would be melted into the glass. In fact, at various stages in the bulb construction sharp-pointed gas flames were used to soften, melt, or seal off the glass bulb or its parts. After the lamp was complete and had been tested, the brass screw base was cemented on, and a wire end soldered to it.

This bulb, with its carbon filament, gave several hundred hours of lighting service. Yet it was only part of a package. Such things as receptacles, wall switches, fuse boxes, and meters had to be provided. An electric generator had to be constructed that could automatically give every light bulb, as it was turned on, the same electrical pressure that the others received. The generator had to handle a thousand bulbs, or ten, or one, as the lights were turned on and off. All these problems and many more were solved by Edison. He was a remarkable research worker, a great inventor, and a brilliant pioneer in the realm of engineering.

D.C. and A.C.

Edison's generators supplied a current that flowed in only one direction. Today, such a flow is called *direct current,* or D.C. Much later, generators were designed to use *alternating current,* or A.C., which periodically reverses the direction of its flow. An alternating-current generator requires a D.C. generator as a source of current. It is called an *exciter.* Today, almost every power plant supplies A.C. current.

PART IV / *Heat and Light, Energy and Power*

In the chapters that follow, a number of ideas and principles related to energy and power, and to heat and light, will be discussed. The story of nineteenth-century physics was, to a great extent, the growing understanding that a relationship existed between heat, light, electricity, and magnetism. From the theoretical work of Faraday, Maxwell, Newton, Young, and others, this knowledge developed, giving rise to radio, television, radar, and other important modern inventions.

Count Rumford

CHAPTER 10

Power, Energy, Heat

The Statics Enigma

The statics enigma is associated with Gilles de Roberval, a French mathematician of the seventeenth century. Roberval invented a balance that behaved in a very interesting way. We might imagine that he had two daughters who were identical twins, and the balance had been made for them to use as a seesaw. But they could not make it go up and down as a good seesaw should. For example, if a cat jumped into the lap of one girl, her end would touch the ground and stay there until the animal was pushed off. Then the beam would go back to where it had been before, and stay there.

Roberval made several modified designs of his balance, and described its strange behavior in a mathematics journal. He chal-

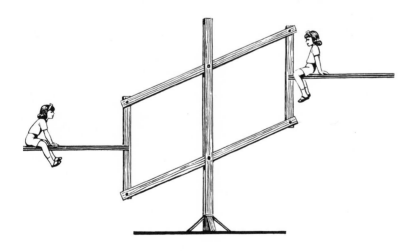

lenged anyone to explain why the arrangement would not operate as a seesaw. One of his variations, with the imaginary twins
added, is shown in the drawing. It is surprising that the girl on the
left does not overbalance her sister.

Later, scientists provided the answer to why the balance
remains motionless or in the same position to which it is moved.
For our purposes, we will name the girls Alice and Beth. If Alice
were to move her end of the beam down to a position one foot
nearer the earth, Beth would rise a foot higher, owing to the
parallel construction of the beam. For any mechanical device
in which the load lifted and the effort used to lift it move
through the same up-and-down distance, the load and effort
must be equal.

Roberval's enigma is an application of the *Law of Machines*.
This law states that a machine does not perform more work than
is put into it. The balance is always a parallelogram—with the
vertical members always remaining vertical. This means that
each horizontal bar will always be horizontal, too. Now, if Alice
goes down 2 feet, Beth, her identical twin, will rise 2 feet. The
work done on Beth is exactly equal to the loss in potential energy
of Alice. In each case, it is the weight of the girl $\times$ 2 feet—an
equilibrium is maintained.

Another application is to be found in the lifting of a stone
by a pulley. In the arrangement shown, the stone can be lifted
by the workman with a force just a third that of its weight, while
the rope passing through the man's hand moves three times the
distance that the stone is raised. The conclusion is this: work is
being done on the stone. The quantity of that work is the weight
in pounds of the stone multiplied by the distance in feet that it
is raised.

The man's work is measured by his upward pull on the
rope multiplied by the distance that it moves through his hands.
Assuming a weightless pulley and neglecting the wasted work
caused by friction, the work done on the weight and the useful

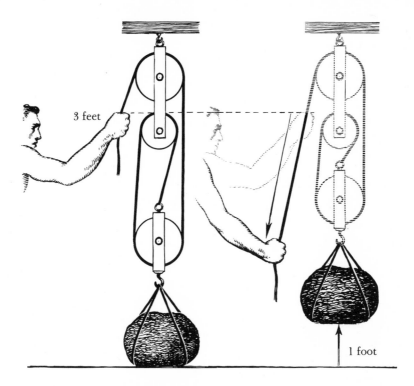

3 feet

1 foot

work done by the man are equal. There are features that require a little extra labor. He must waste work in overcoming friction.

The various simple pieces of equipment that have been used for many centuries to lift heavy weights are numerous. These devices, such as levers, the various pulley combinations, inclined planes, wedges, screws, and heel-and-drum or wheel-and-axle arrangements are called the *simple machines*. For each arrangement, one can calculate the work necessary to lift a particular weight with the machine.

Energy and the Pendulum

Anyone who has gone down an icy hill on a sled knows that it will climb the slope leading up the other side of the

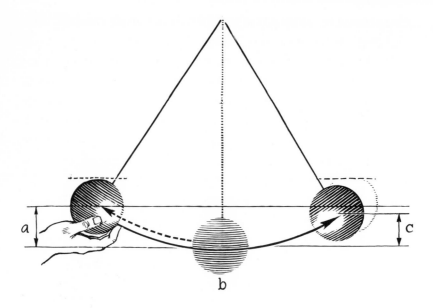

valley if there are no obstructions, but it will not rise higher than the point from which it started. Is this not like a simple machine that raises a weight with the work done by a body in falling? Yes, but there is an additional point. Isaac Newton used a pendulum to illustrate this. In his diagram he showed the center of the weight at *b*. To start the pendulum swinging, the hand lifts the weight to the height of *a*, then releases it. When the hand raises the weight to *a*, work is done on the weight. As the weight swings from *a* to *b*, it trades the energy obtained from this work for the energy of motion. From *b* to *c* it trades the energy of motion for the energy or work needed to raise the weight. But *c* is never higher than *a*, so the trading of one form of energy for another does not create energy.

An Incident of 1873

At the great Fair in Vienna, Austria, in 1873, an electric motor operated by a battery was exhibited not far from a generator operated by water power supplied from outside the exhibition building. As batteries were expensive, the motor was idle much of the time. Some visitor at the Fair suggested that the generator's electricity be applied to the motor. Then the motor could be belted to the generator and run it. One device could operate the other. Surprisingly, the arrangement almost worked. Much the same as in the case of the pendulum, the generator transformed mechanical energy into electrical energy that could be used to run the motor. Then the motor transformed the electrical energy into mechanical energy to run the generator. No energy was created, but since a little power was continually lost as heat, the connected devices lost their initial speed and stopped.

Rumford Takes a New Look at Heat

Heat is one way in which energy can be wasted. Until about the year 1800, it was thought by most scientists that heat might be a very lightweight, colorless fluid that flows from a hot body into a cold one but never goes the other way. Benjamin Thomson, Count Rumford, an Englishman who had been born in Colonial America and, as a soldier, was for a time in the service of the Elector of Bavaria, came to a different conclusion. He had been supervising the boring of brass cannons for the Bavarian Army. He noticed that the duller the tool used in boring out the cannon interior, the hotter the metal became. Horsepower was used as the source of energy for operating the boring tool. He ordered the boring tool to be resharpened. While waiting, he touched the inside of the cannon. His fingers were blistered by the heat. Sitting down, Rumford pondered the situation. If heat is a fluid, how would it be possible to produce it in enormous quantities merely by rubbing two pieces of metal together? But if heat were considered to be a kind of energy like that of motion, it might have been transformed from some other form of power. In fact, the amount of heat seemed to be proportional to the work done by the horse, no matter how efficient the tool was.

Count Rumford made a good estimate of the relation between units of work and heat, but he did not seem to see its significance. James Joule, of England, performed a series of experiments in 1843 and found that the energy exerted by a falling weight would be exchanged for a definite quantity of heat if all the energy were used. The descending weight turned the paddle wheels of a device resembling an egg beater. The water that was churned became warmer. To measure the quantity of heat produced, Joule multiplied the water's weight by the rise in temperature. If, for example, the weight is measured in grams and the temperature in centigrade degrees, the amount of heat is given in calories. Such a calorie is one-thousandth as large an amount of heat as the dietary calorie that gets so much attention today.

The Principle of the Conservation of Energy

One mystery had been bothering scientists ever since Fahrenheit developed the liquid-containing thermometer. If a pan full of very cold cracked ice is heated slowly over a flame, the temperature increases steadily until the melting point is reached. At this point the temperature suddenly stops rising. After all the ice has melted, the temperature goes up again until the water comes to its boiling point. Then the temperature rise stops, not to begin again until all the water has turned to steam. The question is, where did the heat go when the temperature stopped rising?

Eventually, scientists had a simple answer to the question. The heat coming into the pan from the flame is energy. One kind of energy can often be transformed into an equivalent amount of another. When the temperature suddenly stops rising as the ice begins to melt, the heat energy is absorbed and used to overcome some of the forces between molecules, and the solid becomes liquid water. At the higher temperature, the molecules of water that were moving about among each other and were held together as a liquid suddenly break apart, and the liquid becomes a gas, steam. At these two points, then, there was a transformation from one kind of energy, heat, to another, the increased potential energy of the molecules. That transformation could be reversed—condensing steam also releases heat, and heat results as water freezes.

Late in the nineteenth century, this important concept about energy was accepted and a law formulated. Simply: energy can be neither created nor destroyed. It can be transformed from one form to another, but the quantity remains the same. This is the *Law of the Conservation of Energy*.

CHAPTER 11

Light

Various forces and types of energy have been discussed up to this point, but light appears to be different from any of them. It does not seem to have a pull, such as that of gravity; or the ability to do work, such as that of a lifted weight; nor the push and pull of electricity or magnetism. In fact, the rays of the morning sun seem to possess no power at all—we do not have to brace ourselves against them. But, of course, they really do exert pressure—plans are being made today to "sail" spaceships by light pressure.

The Fish That Wasn't There

When light strikes an object's surface, some of it is absorbed and some is turned back, or *reflected*. We see an object because light reflected from it strikes the eye's retina and forms an image. Experience has taught us that light travels in straight lines, and so the brain automatically assumes that this is the case. But sometimes it is fooled.

Every ancient fisherman must have had to learn that a fish appears to be closer to the lake's surface than it really is. A stick partly immersed in water will seem broken at the water line. These optical illusions are due to *refraction*. As long as a light beam travels through a medium of constant optical density, it travels in a straight line, but if it enters a substance with a different optical density, the direction of the beam is altered and it is bent. This change in direction is called refraction.

Lenses

About two thousand years ago, scientists discovered the way smooth surfaces called *plane mirrors* reflect images. These mirrors were made of polished bronze by the Greeks and Romans of ancient times. Many centuries later, glassworkers made plane mirrors out of smooth glass with a polished metal backing. A thousand years or so ago, the Moslem craftsmen had learned how to make curved mirrors, some of which magnified the objects reflected in them. Moslem scientists studied magnifying mirrors, and wrote about their properties and how they could be made. By the time of Galileo, these works had been translated into Latin, and the Venetian glass trade was commercially producing such mirrors as well as the world's finest blown glassware.

When Galileo was at the University of Padua, he was about twenty miles from the glass furnace across the lagoon from Venice. We do not know whether he visited the plant. If he did, he might have been shown a chip of glass shaped like a clamshell and a bit larger than a man's thumb. Some workman may have noticed that chips such as this could be held over the hairs on his hand, magnifying them so that they looked like pig bristles.

Or Galileo may have grown interested in the lenses made for spectacles. These are of two kinds. Sometimes a lens is shaped so that it is thicker in the center and thinner near the edges; this is a *convex lens,* and such a lens magnifies. If a lens is hollowed out in the center, it is called *concave,* and such lenses make objects seen through them appear smaller.

In eyeglasses, convex lenses enable farsighted persons to see close objects better; concave lenses are used for nearsighted persons. Convex lenses can also be used to focus the sun's rays. They were eventually called "burning glasses," for they can set paper on fire. But concave lenses scatter light instead of bringing it to a focus. These effects are due to the fact that light travels in glass only two-thirds as fast as it does in air, but this was not known until a much later time. The rays of the sun are parallel when they reach the earth. These parallel rays are slowed up by the glass of the lens. But since the glass is curved, and thicker in some places than in others, each parallel ray striking the glass is slowed and bent by a different amount. With the con-

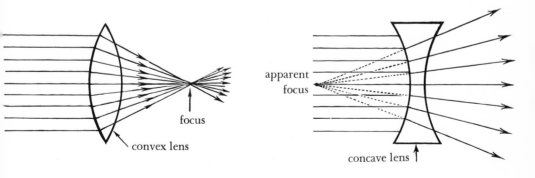

focus

convex lens

apparent focus

concave lens

vex lens, this has the effect of bringing them to a focus and concentrating their heat. Hence the lens is a "burning glass." A concave lens spreads the rays apart in a uniform way so that they appear to come from a focus behind the lens.

Galileo's Tube

One day, word reached Padua that a Dutchman working with lenses had somehow constructed an instrument of two lenses "by means of which visible objects, though very distant from the eye of the observer, were distinctly seen, as if nearby." Galileo had been using only one lens at a time. But after hearing of the new invention he tried combinations of lenses. A pair of convex lenses, when properly placed in conjunction with each other, gave a magnified view of people walking around upside down. Galileo found a more satisfactory combination when he placed a convex lens out at arm's length and a concave lens near the eye. The people were magnified as before, but they walked upright. The lens combination is the same as that used today in opera glasses.

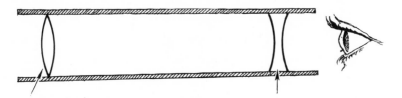

Galileo's next step was to fasten the two lenses firmly in position in a lead tube and arrange the tube on a stand, placing it so that it could be pointed in any direction except straight down.

The device was later called a *telescope,* though many referred to it as the optic tube. Galileo took out no patent on it, nor did he make any secret of its construction. He claimed for it no supernatural powers; he delighted in taking visitors to the highest building in Padua and pointing out from there the sails of boats in the Venetian harbor, twenty miles away. After grinding new lenses, he secured a magnification that enlarged objects 30 times. With this telescope, he was able to make the astronomical discoveries mentioned earlier. There was a strong reaction to Galileo's description of the heavenly bodies he had seen. Many disbelieved the report, calling it trickery. Others refused to look through the tube for fear their eyes would be bewitched and they would see

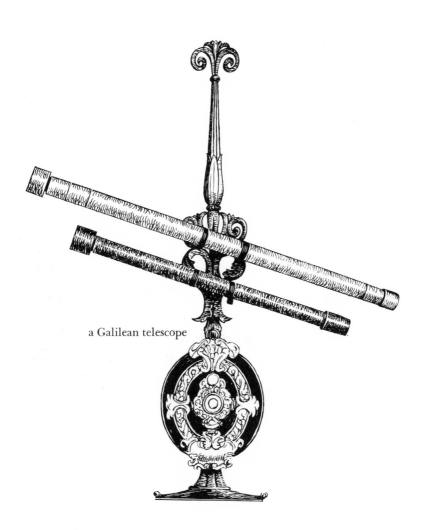

a Galilean telescope

things they should not. But most readers were convinced that he had discovered new worlds.

Newton and the Colors in Sunshine

Newton had a large part in enlarging our knowledge of light. In the winter of the plague year when, under the apple tree, he had worked out the laws of gravitation, the young scientist also studied optics, a field he had become interested in when he was still an undergraduate.

Most of us have had the experience of seeing a ray of early sunshine slip through the shutters, touch the edge of a glass bowl, and burst into sudden color. Perhaps such a sight aroused Newton's interest, for he purchased a prism at a country fair in August of 1666 in order to test the currently held theories about light and color.

Newton darkened his room and made a small hole in the window shutters in order to let in a convenient amount of sun-

light. In front of the hole he placed his prism so that the light it refracted would be cast on the opposite wall. "It was at first a very pleasing diversion to view the vivid and intense colors produced thereby," he wrote. But then he began to concentrate on the oblong band of colors into which the light was dispersed after it passed through the prism. This is called the *solar spectrum,* and Newton listed what he called its original, or primary, colors— red, orange, yellow, green, blue, indigo, and violet.

We may refer to his list as the colors of the rainbow, for they appear against the sky as the sun's rays pass through raindrops that are falling, the drops acting as prisms.

Newton considered that these colors, the major ones and the intermediate shades as well, were present in the sunshine before it reached the prism. The effect of the glass was to separate the various colors as the two changes in the direction of light took place: when it entered the glass, and when it emerged on the other side. Red light was refracted less than yellow light, the yellow less than the violet. Since the colors appearing on the wall showed no gaps, Newton concluded that sunlight is composed of all the colors of the spectrum mixed together in proper proportion. And he suspected that if the dispersed light were passed backward through the prism, white light would appear again. Experiment showed this conclusion to be correct.

Mixing Science with Soap Bubbles

Newton also investigated very carefully the ever-changing display of colors seen in soap bubbles floating in the sunlight. He noticed that yellow might follow red in one area. Then, at another place on the sphere, red might appear again. At one side there might be violet, at another the color would be orange with a streak of green. Always, before the bubble broke, a black patch appeared at the top.

As Newton carefully examined a blown bubble, he understood

the reason for its final collapse. A soap bubble is a film of liquid. Some of the liquid, draining to the bottom, forms a drop. When the top of the film grows thin as the liquid flows down, it will, in time, be too thin to hold together. The bubble, pulling apart, bursts, and it falls as a spray of drops. The color changes before the collapse were evidently associated with the increasing thinness of the film. A film of oil floating on water gives a somewhat similar display of colors, and since floating films do not collapse as bubbles do, they may conveniently be used to find the relation of thickness to color.

Films of oil can also be studied to see what patterns colors will take in them. However, it is too difficult to control the thickness of oil layers. Instead, such material as plates of glass and controlled thin films are used. For example, oil film can be viewed with a light source giving only yellow light. For the yellow light source, an alcohol lamp with salt added to the alcohol can be used. In that light, the yellow reflected from the oil film is in bands of even thickness, with black spaces edging the color. These dark areas are the parts of the film that reflect colors other than yellow.

Newton made very extensive studies of the color patterns seen when light passed through thin films. He first used films of air formed by laying the convex side of a very long-focus telescope lens against a piece of glass with a plane surface, passing light sources of different colors through them. When he looked through the film of air, he saw a series of rings emanating from a bright central circular portion. We now know that the rings begin at a region where the distance between the two pieces of glass is one-quarter that of the wavelength of the light being used. Thus, the size of a given ring depends on the wavelength of the light passing through the lenses. Newton said:

> *"I found the circles which the red light made to be mani-*
> *festly bigger than those which were made by the blue and*

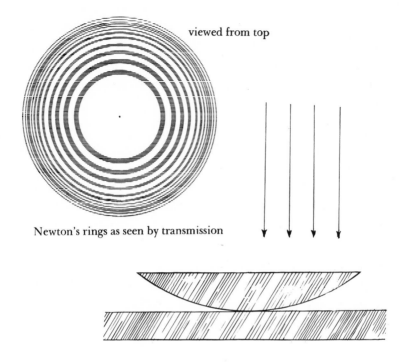

viewed from top

Newton's rings as seen by transmission

*violet. And it was very pleasant to see them gradually swell
or contract accordingly as the color of the light was changed."*

How Thomas Young Supplied the Idea of Waves

Word of Newton's rings aroused immediate interest among
scientists. Many hurried to make the same arrangement of equipment that Newton had used in order to conduct their own experiments. But for about a hundred years there was no truly
satisfactory theory of how these rings are formed.

Newton presented an elaborate explanation of the cause of
the rings. He thought they evidently had a close connection with
the thickness of the space between the glass sheets. Although at
one time he came close to understanding the phenomenon, he
could not do so fully because he did not know the way light

travels. He believed that a light ray was composed of a number of infinitesimal particles that moved very fast in a straight path.

In 1803, an English physicist and physician, Thomas Young, came to a different conclusion. He believed that light traveled in waves much like the waves of the sea. If one end of a rope is fastened to a wall and the other end is moved rapidly up and down, a series of fluctuations passes along the rope. These are *waves*. The *wavelength* is determined by the horizontal distance between two high crests; the horizontal distance between a high crest and a low crest would be half of one wavelength.

Sometimes, in the open sea, two waves meet "in step" with one another, merge, and a new, stronger wave results. At other times, two waves can be so much out of step that one will destroy the other, and no wave moves on after the collision. Young called this the principle of *interference*.

Now, when this idea is applied to Newton's rings, it is possible to see how they are formed. If a beam of red light strikes the top glass at an angle, some of it is reflected, and some passes

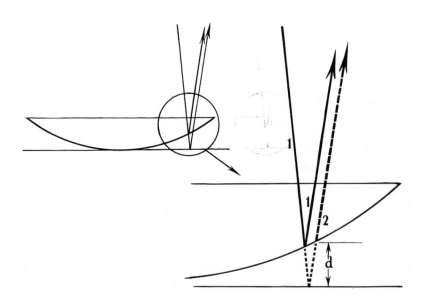

through the glass to the surface of the second piece. Here again, reflection occurs, and the reflected light passes back at another angle through the upper glass, emerging into the air. Thus light is reflected to the eye by a shorter path from the upper glass and a longer path from the lower one. If the light wave moving along the shorter path emerges just half a wavelength ahead of the other, the waves interfere with each other; the glass surface appears black. The same thing happens when the first light wave is 1½ or 2½ wavelengths ahead of the second. But if the first wave is exactly one wavelength ahead, or two, or three, the two light waves merge, reinforcing one another, and the glass appears red. Thus, the rings, with dark spaces in between them, are formed. Young found that the wavelength of red was about 1/36,000 of an inch and that of violet about 1/60,000 of an inch. These are the limits of wavelengths that the eye can see.

How Fizeau Measured the Velocity of Light

Light travels so rapidly that it can go around the earth more than four times while one says "Jack Robinson." To be able to measure anything moving that fast might seem impossible. Galileo tried it and failed; so did others. In 1666, Olaus Roemer, a Danish astronomer, was more successful. He had been studying the motions of Jupiter's satellites as they revolved around the planet, passing behind it, and then coming around to cross its illuminated face. Roemer noticed that it took a satellite more time to pass behind Jupiter when the earth was receding from that planet than when the earth was approaching it. From this discrepancy, Roemer arrived at an approximation of the speed of light. While rather far from the true figure, his was the first successful attempt to make the measurement.

In 1849, Armand Fizeau, a French physicist, obtained a more accurate figure. He prepared a new kind of experiment to measure the velocity of light. Two telescopes were set up, one in a house in Suresnes, a suburb of Paris, the other on the hill of Montmartre, a bit over five miles away. The telescopes were put in position so that the image of the objective of each was formed at the focus of the other.

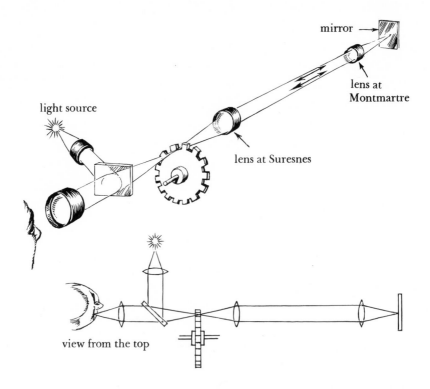

mirror

lens at
Montmartre

light source

lens at Suresnes

view from the top

The Suresnes telescope picked up a beam of light cast by a lamp and reflected it toward the telescope on Montmartre. This instrument, which had a mirror placed at its focus, reflected the light back to the first telescope, in Suresnes. Before the light could enter the Suresnes telescope, it had to pass a rapidly turning toothed disc. The telescope opening and the teeth were the same width. Thus, as the wheel was turned, the light flashed into the telescope as one tooth moved out of the way only to be stopped by the next one. If the wheel had 50 teeth, the light would be able to pass through 50 times every revolution and would be stopped

50 times. If the wheel was spun fast enough, the light that had passed into the first instrument when a tooth moved would be reflected back by the Montmartre telescope in time to be blocked by the next tooth. When the speed of the disc and the number of teeth were known, the velocity of light could be calculated. Fizeau arrived at a figure that we now know to be about 5 per cent too high.

Scientists continued trying to improve Fizeau's experiment. Finally, in 1927, the American physicist Albert A. Michelson, by refining the apparatus, arrived at a figure of about 186,254 miles per second for the velocity of light, almost exactly the figure accepted today—186,281 miles a second, when traveling through a vacuum.

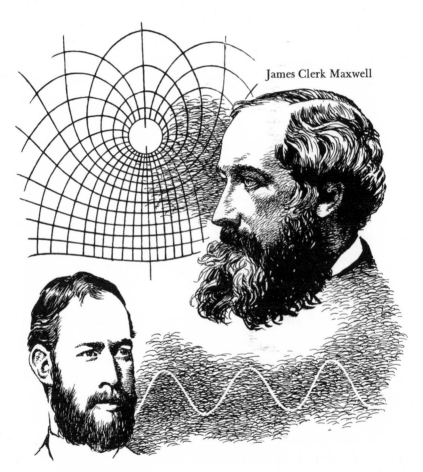

James Clerk Maxwell

Heinrich R. Hertz

CHAPTER 12

The Full Spectrum of Radiant Energy

At about the same time that the wavelengths of the spectrum colors were determined, it was recognized that other invisible rays are reaching the earth. Some have longer wavelengths than the red of the spectrum; some have shorter wavelengths than the violet. Light is a kind of energy, just as electricity and heat are. It is known as a form of *radiant energy*. Examples of invisible radiant energy are radio waves, X rays, and ultraviolet and infrared rays.

Ultraviolet and Infrared

If a black-and-white photograph is made of a brilliant rainbow, the curve of the bow will be perfectly shaped on the print. However, the bow will appear a little lower in the sky than we see it. This is because the deep red that for us forms the top of the bow is missing. To make up for it, the photo shows a dark area on the inside of the bow, beyond the violet. These rays are even shorter in wavelength than the shortest visible violet rays. The film chemicals are sensitive to this *ultraviolet*—"beyond the violet"—light. On the other hand, the chemicals do not respond to some reds that we do see. Vision may differ among the species of the animal world, as well. It seems probable that some insects can actually "see" ultraviolet radiation, for they move toward the end of a long tunnel that is dark except for the end, which is illuminated by an ultraviolet light source. As early as 1801, scientists began to note the existence of this invisible light.

A year before the first observation of ultraviolet rays, Sir William Herschel, the English astronomer, discovered the *infrared* —"below-the-red"—light. These waves are longer in wavelength than any we can see. Like the ultraviolet, they reach the earth from the sun. All radiant energy produces a certain amount of heat in the bodies it strikes. Herschel was performing an experiment to find out the difference in heat produced by the colors of the spectrum. With a black cloth wrapped around the bulb of a thermometer, he placed the bulb, in turn, at each primary color of the spectrum. The cloth absorbed the heat and transmitted it to the thermometer. He found that the temperature rose least at the violet end and most at the red. But the heating effect did not stop at the red. It went on into an area where the eye would not have known that rays existed. The ultraviolet and infrared "colors" are now considered part of the solar spectrum.

Maxwell and Radiant Electric Waves

James Clerk Maxwell, a brilliant Scottish mathematical physicist, devoted much of his life to the study of electromagnetic forces. He began by trying to translate into mathematical equations Faraday's ideas about the lines of force around magnets and electromagnets.

Maxwell may have had his attention called to a happening not uncommon around electric machines, in which the lightning-like discharge at the machine terminals triggers the discharge of a fully charged Leyden jar or condenser several feet away. Maxwell boldly suggested that all electromagnetic energy travels through space in waves at the speed of light. He may have identified this electromagnetic radiation moving through the air from the electric machine as the energy which set off the Leyden jar's discharge. From Maxwell's work it was possible to construct an electromagnetic theory of light, as well. It was a strange idea then, and was not readily accepted. Becoming interested in the mathematical approach to his suggestion of a wave motion, Maxwell worked out equations for the conditions under which an electromagnetic wave moving through a fully charged Leyden jar would cause it to discharge.

He predicted that whenever electric charges were accelerated, these charges would radiate energy. This energy would appear in the region around the charges as an electromagnet field and radiate outward as an electromagnetic disturbance. To carry this energy, he postulated the existence of the ether. When Maxwell calculated the speed with which such waves should travel through the ether, he found that they would have the same speed as light. These waves would have their origin in accelerated, or oscillating, charges, such as those moving in a spark discharge from a Leyden jar. And these waves, in turn, could cause charges to oscillate when they encountered them. The waves were changing electric and magnetic fields which would induce currents in conductors. Thus, he predicted the existence of radio long before it was developed.

Maxwell's first ideas were announced in 1864. Twenty-three years later, the waves that he had predicted would be found were produced in the laboratory. In that year, 1887, the German physicist Heinrich R. Hertz proved the existence of electromagnetic radiation. He had set up, with an induction coil, an oscillating electric circuit—that is, one of high-frequency alternating current. This current surged into first one, then another of two metal balls connected to the coil and separated from one another by an air gap. The periodic sharp, crackling discharge of a spark resulted. It traveled across the gap between the balls.

Maxwell had predicted that each oscillation would produce one electromagnetic wave. In order to detect these waves, Hertz set up, a few feet away from the oscillating current, a loop of copper wire with a small air gap at one point. To one of the ends of the wire, he attached a little brass sphere. Then he adjusted the loop so that the other end of the wire was only a minute

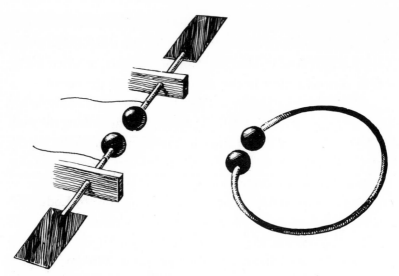

distance away from the brass ball. Just as the electric current in the induction coil created electromagnetic radiation, so the radiation should be able to create a current in the loop, or second coil. That is exactly what happened. Hertz was able to detect very small sparks jumping across the gap of the loop. He also showed that these waves were reflected, refracted, and absorbed exactly like light waves.

Here, although Hertz did not realize it, was a means of wireless communication. The news of the experiment spread rapidly, and those who had ignored or disbelieved Maxwell's mathematical work now acknowledged that he had been right in his predictions.

Marconi Applies a Scientist's Dream

By 1894, the physicist Oliver Lodge, of England, had demonstrated in his science laboratory how some changes in the equipment used by Hertz would make the arrangement useful for short-distance signaling.

Perhaps Lodge did not have in mind any particular function where signaling with electric waves would be vitally important. The Italian scientist Guglielmo Marconi did. It was important for ships at sea, out beyond the range where signal-flashing with lights or mirrors could reach them. It was needed when fogs closed down, cutting off all view of landmarks or of the stars, or when a ship was in distress or lost in the great expanses of the ocean.

Trained as an electrical engineer, the twenty-one-year-old Marconi happened to read an article, in 1894, describing the work of Hertz, who had died earlier in the year. Stimulated by the article, Marconi set to work trying to develop a means of using electromagnetic waves for communication. Soon after, he went to England to learn at first hand what was being done by Lodge and others. With his own funds, he set up an experimental shop, and his life's career began to take shape. In 1896, in England, Marconi patented his first *wireless telegraph* apparatus. With it, a signal could be sent in Morse code a distance of nine miles across space without the use of wires. The device was useful for some ship-to-ship or ship-to-shore messages, but it was still not powerful enough to reach vessels far out at sea or those widely separated from one another.

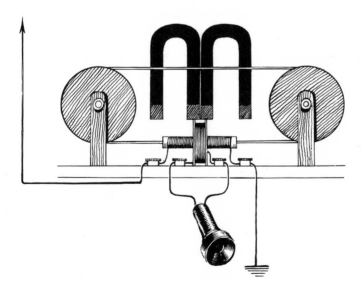

Marconi continued to improve his invention. In 1897, he sent a signal from land to a ship 12 miles at sea. In 1898, the signal distance was increased to 18 miles. Finally, in 1901, he succeeded in sending a message from the southwest corner of England across the Atlantic Ocean to Newfoundland. In 1909, for his work in the development of wireless telegraphy, Marconi shared the Nobel Prize with the German physicist Karl Ferdinand Braun, who had also contributed to the technique of radio.

In 1901, the wireless telegraph was still able only to send out the relatively simple pulses of the Morse code. But a few years later the wireless telephone, or radiotelephone, was developed. Soon, the wireless receiver could pick up the transmitted electrical signals obtained from the sound impulses of speech and music.

No one person or any single group created the wireless telephone or was responsible for expanding it into radio broadcasting. As in the Bell telephone, the sound vibrations were changed to electrical signals by the wireless telephone, and these signals were impressed on the electromagnetic waves. Traveling with almost the speed of light, the vibrations were directed to the receiver, where they were again transformed into sound. There are two ways to handle the impression of sound vibrations on the waves. The earlier form, called *amplitude modulation,* or AM, affects the height of the up-and-down swing of the wave. A later method, called *frequency modulation,* or FM, temporarily affects the length of the wave.

The great success of the telegraph lay in the relay arrangement by which a faint sound at the receiver was magnified by the relay into a loud, clear sound. The wireless telephone, and later the radio, if they were to transmit beyond walkie-talkie distance, needed an even more sensitive relay arrangement, capable of even greater magnification. This was developed by the American inventor Lee De Forest.

He used a modification of a *vacuum tube.* The simplest vacuum tube is called a *diode.* It was developed in the early years of the twentieth century by the English electrical engineer Sir John

Ambrose Fleming. The diode consists of a tube, usually metal or glass, from which much of the air has been pumped, creating a vacuum. Within the tube is a *filament,* or *cathode,* connected to a source of electricity, which heats the filament. The heated filament emits electrons. Also in the tube is a metallic element called a plate, or anode. When the plate and the filament are connected to a source of electricity, which makes the plate positive and the filament negative a current flows between them.

De Forest improved the diode with his invention of the *triode.* It consists of a vacuum tube containing the cathode, the plate, and another part as well—the *grid,* a mesh of very fine wire between the positively and negatively charged elements.

If the grid is negatively charged, it will repel the electrons being emitted by the cathode, and only a few will get through to the plate. The current flow out of the vacuum tube will be very weak. However, if the grid is positively charged, it will attract a large number of electrons. Since the grid is largely open space, most of the electrons will pass through it and flow on to the anode. Then the current flow is *amplified,* or made stronger. The triode is the basis of the well-known radio tube.

Just as the wavelengths of different colors vary, there are many radio-wave wavelengths. The first that were used are long—from 800 feet to five miles. Such waves, if beamed diagonally at the sky, do not pass on into outer space to become lost. The upper atmosphere acts as a reflector; they bounce back toward the earth, and thus can be detected by receivers hundreds of miles away from the broadcasting station.

When television and frequency modulation were developed, the wavelengths chosen as highly suitable were shorter than those of the amplitude-modulation broadcasting zone. They have wavelengths of from a little over one foot up to 800 feet, and cannot be bounced against the reflecting zone in the atmosphere. Their beaming has to be direct from transmitter to receiver.

Radar Scanning of the Sky

At the beginning of World War II, English physicists, who had been investigating the electromagnetic waves in the wavelength range between an inch and a foot, were asked to increase the intensity of their research in order to develop a militarily practical system of aircraft detection that would work when enemy planes were not visible, either because of their distance or because of unfavorable weather conditions like clouds or fog. From that work, the *radar* scanning of the skies developed.

A radar beam could be sent from an earth location, sweeping across the sky. It could not be seen as it passed through light clouds and penetrated fogs. Much as a searchlight beam would do, radar showed up German airplanes as they swept toward England's shores in battle formation. The pilots of these planes did not at first know that their path was being followed, for the beams shining upon them gave no hint of light or color. Down on the earth, as the reflected waves returned with the speed of light, there were special receivers with maplike screens that indicated any objects the beam might strike. From the changing screen picture, the size of the object, its speed, and its location could be determined. Today, radar is an important factor in military defense. It has also been used in weather studies—to detect tornadoes in their beginning stages, for example—and the future may bring more uses as man explores space.

Roentgen's Mystery Rays

Other radiant energy exists. One type has a short wavelength, much shorter than even ultraviolet waves. The main character in the story of its discovery is Wilhelm Roentgen, professor of physics at the University of Würzburg, in Germany. The time is 1895.

Professor Roentgen, like many other scientists of his day, was investigating the discharge of electricity in cathode-ray tubes, such as the Crookes tube. In the course of his studies, Roentgen noticed that a paper screen coated with a crystalline substance, barium platinocyanide, placed a little more than two feet away from the tube, gave off a bright fluorescent light while the tube was in operation. The screen glowed even when the tube was wrapped in black paper. It still fluoresced when its coated side was turned away from the tube. Moreover, the fluorescence lasted only as long as the electrical discharge did, stopping when it stopped. There must be some mystery rays, originating in the tube, coming through the glass, and setting the screen aglow when they struck it.

Roentgen, who was a careful experimenter, thoroughly investigated these *X rays,* as he called them. He found that they penetrated lightweight substances deeply, but were blocked by heavy substances like lead. He designed and had constructed a special X-ray tube that would be useful for his studies.

In time, it was shown that the very short X-ray band of wavelengths ranged from, at one extreme, a ray that would scarcely throw the shadow of a rose petal, to a ray, at the other extreme, that could penetrate a steel rail and show any flaws in the interior. X rays are widely used now in medical and dental examinations and in industry. The identification of *gamma rays,* even shorter in wavelength and more penetrating than X rays, was made by Ernest Rutherford, and will be discussed in Chapter 14.

To conclude this story of the growth of physics, some of the revolutionary advances of the twentieth century will be examined briefly. As a sampling of the new ideas, the stories of three men will be presented: a great theorist, Einstein; a noted experimenter, Rutherford; and, finally, a man who made contributions both in theory and in experiment, Fermi.

Albert Einstein

CHAPTER 13

Einstein

Two short formulas, the shorthand for two laws of nature, are at the heart of physics:

$$F = ma$$
$$E = mc^2$$

The first of these is Newton's second law of motion, which was encountered earlier in a different form. It states that the rate at which the velocity of a body changes (the acceleration, a), multiplied by the mass of that body (m), is equal to the force on the body (F). This simple statement—$F = ma$—tells us about the motions of automobiles and atoms, of the earth and of billiard balls. It is the foundation of mechanics.

The second formula, $E = mc^2$, is very different. It relates the energy (E) of an object to its mass (m) and to an unchanging constant, the square of the velocity of light (c). Though Newton studied energy and mass and the properties of light, he never put the three together. That task was accomplished by Albert Einstein, and with this simple formula he helped unlock the energy of the atom.

Albert Einstein was born in Ulm, Germany, in 1879. As a child he lived in Munich, and from the time he was fifteen in Milan; later he studied in Switzerland. We can imagine Professor Einstein in 1946, toward the end of his great career. He is in his book-lined office at the Institute for Advanced Study, in Princeton, New Jersey. Dressed in an old sweater, pipe in mouth, he is thinking about the adventure of his life.

It was a great adventure, not of travel and daring deeds but of the mind, of thoughts that stretched from the infinitely small to the very boundaries of the universe. Reminiscing, Einstein recalls his childhood. When he was four or five, his father showed him a compass. Here was a mystery. The other wonders of the world—the falling of apples, the wind and the rain, the moon and the stars—were too familiar to make an impression. However, the determination of the compass needle to point north without any visible cause was surprising to the young boy. It started him on a career of thought.

Another youthful adventure occurred at the age of twelve, when his teacher gave him a book on geometry. In it Einstein found how it was possible, starting from a few simple assumptions, to show a great wealth of relationships by pure thought. To learn the properties of triangles and squares, it is necessary only to think about them in a logical way; the result will be a more exact truth than direct measurement could give. Geometry was only the introduction, and within a few years the young Einstein became familiar with the principles of mathematics.

At seventeen, he entered the Federal Polytechnic school in Zurich, Switzerland, where he studied mathematics and physics. He spent most of his time in the laboratory, fascinated by his direct contact with the behavior of nature. Here he could study nature in a pure, simple way. He could control it, eliminate confusion, and seek answers to specific problems.

The wealth of subjects he found at the Polytechnic posed a problem not unlike that faced by the mythical Buridan's ass. Offered two equally attractive bundles of hay, the ass dies of starvation while trying to decide which to eat first. Which of the many fields of physics and mathematics was the young Einstein to settle on as his life's work? He decided not to become a specialist and to concern himself with those problems that would lead to a deeper insight into the laws of nature. Instead of filling his mind with details, he planned to keep it free to ponder the fundamentals.

Admirable as it sounds, there was a rub in this approach; to graduate as a scientist, he had to take examinations. To pass these, he had to cram his head full of all kinds of specialized information. After graduating from the Polytechnic, it took a whole year before his brain was sufficiently clear to think again about the mysteries of nature.

The physics Einstein learned in school was governed by fixed rules. There were Newton's laws of motion and the necessary masses and forces—that was all. The rest could be predicted by mathematics. This simple, mechanical picture of the universe, based on the work of Galileo, Newton, and others, was beginning to fall apart at the end of the nineteenth century. Einstein contributed much toward building the new physics.

From 1902 until 1909, he was a patent examiner in Berne, Switzerland. How important the patents he examined were is not known. His reexamination of physics, however, led to unprecedented results, and the year 1905 is of particular importance. During this year Einstein wrote five papers that revolutionized three fields of physics. He showed how to determine the size of atoms, he proved that light was not only a wave but also a particle, and he developed the theory of relativity. Any one of these contributions would have ranked Einstein among the great men of physics. The fact that he was able to make all three within a single year while working at the patent office is astounding.

Einstein's least radical contribution during that great year had to do with the size of atoms. In 1827, the British botanist Robert Brown had studied pollen grains under his microscope. Pollen is the male genetic material of plants, which is carried by bees or the wind to the female part of the flower. To his amazement, Brown found that when the little pollen grains were suspended in water, they were in constant motion, now jiggling this way, now that. What made them move? Obviously, they had no legs. It was not even necessary to use pollen. Any small particles suspended in a fluid perform the erratic dance known as *Brownian motion*. For almost a hundred years, people looking through micro-

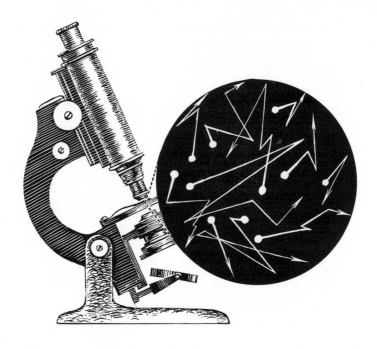

scopes had wondered about it. It remained for Einstein not only to find an answer but to use the pattern of the dance to measure the size of molecules and of the atoms that compose them.

By the time Einstein attended the Polytechnic, most scientists believed that nature was not continuous but, rather, that matter was composed of atoms. In a gas, these atoms move about freely. In a solid, the atoms are firmly bound to each other by strong forces; in a liquid, they are able to move around while more loosely tied together. If a small, solid object is placed in a liquid, it will be jostled about by the ceaseless random motion of the liquid's molecules. If the particle is sufficiently large, the pushing of myriad molecules against it will average out, and the particle will remain at rest. If it is smaller, however, at one moment the shoving from one side may be stronger than the shoving from the other side, and so it will move a little. The next instant it may be pushed more from the opposite side, and it will thus reverse its track.

To know the details of the Brownian dance, one would have to know the individual motions of all the molecules and atoms that are shoving the particle. Einstein showed, however, that one could study the problem in a statistical way and thus determine the size of the liquid atoms. From past experience, an insurance company can predict what fraction of the population will die in any period, but they do not know *who* will die. In the same way, by measuring the average distance the particle had moved in a given time, Einstein was able to determine how often it had been pushed. Thus he was able to calculate how much bigger the particle was than the atoms. His reasoning was so clear, and the demonstration of Brownian motion so convincing, that the last of the skeptics were finally convinced of the atomicity of matter.

Einstein's second contribution during 1905 had to do with a different type of particle, the light particle. From earliest time, man has wondered about the nature of light. What is it that is emitted by the sun and then scattered and reflected by objects to impinge on our eye and stimulate the optic nerves? Newton thought that light is composed of particles which move at great speed. Others thought that light consisted of waves moving through an invisible, very thin substance, the ether, extending throughout space. Indeed, some of Newton's own work supported this theory of the wave nature of light, for, as noted earlier, the colors he saw in the soap films resulted from light waves. Later, Maxwell formulated the laws of waves resulting from oscillating electric currents. When he worked out the speed at which these then unknown electrical waves would travel, it turned out to be the same as the speed of light as measured by Fizeau. So ordinary light was nothing more or less than electromagnetic waves of very short wavelength.

As we have seen, Hertz was the first to produce the waves predicted by Maxwell. During his experiments, he accidentally dis-

covered that a spark gap could be made to fire if the metal was illuminated by the light from another spark. Soon it was found
that any metal surface, if illuminated by ultraviolet light, would
give off negative electricity. It would do this even in a vacuum.
Evidently, when the metal was illuminated it gave off units of
negative electric charge—i.e., electrons.

Everywhere, physicists in their laboratories were busy
studying the liberation of electricity by light, but the more
they learned, the harder it became to explain the effect. Scientists tried various metals using light of different wavelengths. As
might be expected, the amount of electricity liberated depended
on the intensity of the light used. This liberation of electrons by
light is called the *photoelectric effect;* it can be used to build an
exposure meter. When light hits a metal, it liberates electrons
which produce an electric current, which is measured by a
simple current meter. All light, however, does not act in the
same way. There is a limiting wavelength for each metal above
which the substance will not emit any electrons, regardless of
the light's intensity. The shorter the wavelength, the more
energy the electrons have.

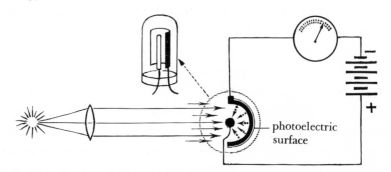

photoelectric
surface

The rate at which a wave transmits energy depends on its
amplitude, or size, and its *frequency,* or the number of wavelengths
per second. Waves on the ocean become dangerous when the wave
crests tower over a ship. The sound of a phonograph becomes annoying when the volume is too high, but the piercing high fre-

quencies of a violin may be more annoying than the low frequencies of a bass fiddle. The speed of the waves is the product of their frequency and their wavelength. Since all light waves travel at the same speed, high-frequency waves have short wavelengths, and low-frequency waves have long wavelengths. This means that the limiting wavelength above which electrons were not emitted corresponded to a lowest frequency, which produced this effect. It also means that the higher the frequency, the more energy the electrons have. Yet the electrons have mass, and should be less capable of responding to high frequencies than to low frequencies.

To explain this, Einstein assumed that light waves can also be considered as bundles of energy (later called *photons*), and that the energy of each bundle was greater as its wavelength grew shorter. He also postulated that to produce the photoelectric effect, a photon of light, when it struck the metal, would give all of its energy to a single electron. Normally the electron is trapped in the metal, and to escape requires a certain amount of energy. If the energy of the photon was sufficient, the electron could jump out, and a number of escaping electrons could produce a current. If the wavelength is sufficiently short, each photon gives rise to exactly one electron. In one stroke, Einstein's simple theory explained the strange behavior of the photoelectric effect that scientists had been puzzling over since Hertz first observed it.

Light, which Newton considered to be a particle and which Maxwell described as a wave, now was understood to have a split personality. When it is absorbed in a substance it is a particle, or photon; during its travels through space it is a wave. Others have shown that when light is emitted from a light source it also behaves as a discrete particle. The old idea that a wave is a wave and a particle is something else had to be abandoned. Nor did this dual nature stop with light, for later it was found that particles such as electrons also behaved on occasion like waves. Thus, the simple mechanics of Newton was supplemented by wave mechanics. As long as anything as large as apples or moons is considered, the wave nature of matter is of no consequence, and Newton's laws are perfectly valid. When we look at atoms and the parts of which they are composed, however, the wave nature of these particles becomes important. Einstein's theory of the photoelectric effect opened the way to an understanding of the split personality of nature—waves and particles.

Einstein's greatest contribution during this productive year was the *special theory of relativity*. When the ordinary world is left for the microworld of atoms, electrons, and photons, the simple mechanics of Newton have to be left behind, too. Not only do Newton's mechanics become invalid when we look at the very small, but also when we consider anything moving very fast. For some time it had been known that physical theories seem not to be valid as the speed of light is approached, but it remained for Einstein to bring the pieces of the puzzle together in his special theory of relativity.

An imaginary flight in a jet plane will help explain the basic idea of relativity. We sit down, fasten our seat belt, and, with a great surge of power, the giant plane accelerates down the runway for the takeoff. As the plane increases its speed, we are pushed back against our seat—or, rather, the seat is pushing us forward so that our bodies accelerate at the same rate as the plane. At this stage no instruments are necessary; our senses tell us very clearly what is going on.

Once cruising speed is reached, the seat-belt sign goes off, and if the air is smooth, we feel no discomfort, no further sense of acceleration of motion. If a passenger had slept through the takeoff, he would not know without looking out of the window whether he was still on the ground or up in the air. Would instruments be able to indicate the plane's motion? Of course, the cockpit is loaded with gauges to give just that sort of information. All of them, however, depend on sensors outside the plane. They get their data from the air or receive radio signals from transmitters on the ground.

In order to find out how fast the plane is going, perhaps it is still possible to use only information determined within the plane; perhaps the velocity of light might be used. Until Einstein's work, light was considered to be a wave oscillation of the ether. If that were so, the plane's velocity relative to the ether would be, say, 600 miles per hour more than it is when standing still. Thus, if the velocity of light is measured in the plane, the difference between it and the velocity of light as measured on the ground should give the plane's speed.

The critical experiment in determining whether or not this was so was performed in Cleveland in 1887 by two Americans, Albert A. Michelson and Edwin W. Morley. Obviously, they had neither a jet nor any other plane at their disposal, for the Wright brothers' first powered flight was still sixteen years in the future, and even it hardly offered sufficient speed. Instead, they used the spaceship that all of us have been traveling on since birth—the earth. As the earth travels around the sun, moving at about one-ten-thousandth the velocity of light, or 18½ miles per second, it traverses the ether. By comparing the speed of light along the line of the earth's travel, and again at right angles to it, Michelson and Morley were not able to detect any difference. Perhaps the earth was at rest relative to the ether on that particular day. They repeated the experiment at various times of the year when the earth was moving in different directions relative to the stars. Regardless of when they performed their experiment, they were never able to detect any difference.

The constancy of the velocity of light was very puzzling. An Irishman and a Dutchman, G. F. Fitzgerald and H. A. Lorentz, offered a possible explanation. The experiments could be explained if one assumed that the apparatus, due to its motion along with the earth through the ether, shrinks by exactly the amount necessary to make the beam of light seem to travel at the same velocity. Then the figure for the velocity of light would always be the same. It would be impossible to detect the shrinkage of the equipment, since any measuring stick laid alongside the apparatus would shrink by the same amount. The Fitzgerald-Lorentz contraction explained the results of the Michelson-Morley experiment, but the arguments for the contraction were not very convincing.

At this stage Einstein was able to break through the confusion with a few simple ideas. Ten years before, when he was only sixteen, he had toyed with the basic clue to the dilemma: Suppose I shine a beam from my flashlight off into space. It will travel with the velocity *c.* If I now run after it with the same velocity, it would appear that the light beam was standing still and was merely an electrical oscillation fixed in space. However, nobody has ever seen an electrical wave standing still and, according to Maxwell's equations, such a thing would not happen.

In his paper of 1905 on the special theory of relativity, Einstein showed how the problem of the constancy of the velocity of light could be solved if two very simple assumptions are made. First, it must be assumed that the laws of nature are the same in any two systems moving in a uniform way with respect to each other. Thus, if a laboratory is set up in a fast jet plane, all experiments in the plane will give the same results that they would if the plane were standing still on the ground. The second assumption is that the velocity of light is independent of the velocity of its source.

These assumptions are as simple and as reasonable as those made in the geometry book that Einstein read when he was twelve. The conclusions one can draw from them are no less remarkable than those in the geometry text. As long as the motions of two systems relative to each other are slow compared to the velocity of light, nothing is changed. When the speed of light is approached, however, all kinds of weird things happen. Measuring sticks shrink, masses become heavier, and clocks run slower. These changes, of course, are all relative.

If two twins are moving very fast with respect to one another,

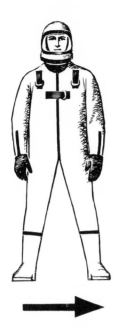 

each would appear perfectly normal to a traveller moving with him. However, his twin would appear flattened out, his pulse beat would be slower, and he would appear to be much heavier. This increase in mass is related to his increase in kinetic energy by the famous formula $E = mc^2$.

All this seems rather fantastic. To the nuclear physicist, however, it is commonplace, for he deals with small bits of matter that are traveling at almost the speed of light. These speeds are produced by cyclotrons and other atom-smashing machines. The faster these particles move, the heavier they become. Some of the particles are very unstable, like soap bubbles, and would explode in an instant if they were standing still. The faster they move, however, the longer they last before they blow up.

At the time Einstein proposed his theory, it aroused all kinds of arguments. People applied relativity to different fields that had nothing to do with it. There were believers and nonbelievers. The fact that Einstein had treated time in a way similar to his treatment of the three dimensions of space gave rise to talk of a mysterious fourth dimension. However, most of this popular discussion was nonsense. Einstein had made two simple assumptions about nature. From these he had derived new laws predicting some things that were old and proven and others that were new, such as the slowing down of time and the increase in an object's mass. Whether Einstein was right or wrong could not be settled by arguments, popular or learned. The final judge of science is nature, which must be consulted by careful experiments in order to see if the answers are in agreement with Einstein's prediction. To date, every experiment carried out has indicated that the special theory of relativity, first proposed by Einstein in 1905, is correct within the limits of experimental error.

Thus the train of thought started by a simple compass needle led to the discovery of a new law of nature, the knowledge of which has transformed the world. To learn more of that transformation, we will look over the shoulder of an experimenter who played with the heart of the atom—the nucleus.

Ernest Rutherford

CHAPTER 14

Rutherford

So far, the history of physics has taken place almost exclusively in Europe. Now we shall consider a man who came from New Zealand, at the opposite end of the world—Ernest Rutherford, who was born in 1871. Like Newton, he grew up on a farm. He did well in school and won a scholarship to Canterbury University College, in Christchurch, New Zealand. There, he became interested in Hertz's radio waves. In a small, vacant cellar at the college, he studied these waves and detected them by using iron wires.

In his experiments, Rutherford was forced to rely on his own ingenuity, for even the primitive scientific apparatus of that time was scarce in New Zealand. In one of the first papers he presented before the local scientific society, he described a very simple apparatus to measure time intervals as short as 1/100,000 of a second. He accomplished this difficult feat in a very simple manner. A cylindrical weight with a hole through which a vertical wire passed was allowed to fall down the wire from a height of three feet. At the bottom, it hit two copper bars and, in so doing, opened electrical contacts on the bars. The exact position of one of them could be altered with a screw. First, the apparatus was adjusted so that both contacts would open at the same instant. Then, by turning the screw, one bar was lowered slightly, so that the weight would hit it an instant after the contact of the first bar had been opened. From the velocity of the weight, calculated by the laws of Newton, and from the displacement of the bar,

Rutherford could calculate the time that had elapsed between the opening of the first and the second contact.

With this simple and elegant apparatus, Rutherford was able to study magnetization during very short intervals of time. All through his career, he showed the same brilliance in obtaining important results with very simple apparatus. After graduating, Rutherford taught at a boys' school. This was a trying experience for him; the boys had difficulty understanding his teaching, and he had problems keeping order in the classroom. With time, he would undoubtedly have become a good high-school teacher, but fortune singled him out for a different role.

The story of how this young man from the other end of the world was to journey to Cambridge, England, and become a pioneer in the new physics had its actual beginning in 1851, twenty years before Rutherford was born. In that year, England held a great exhibition, the first world's fair, in London at the Crystal Palace, under the sponsorship of Queen Victoria's husband, Prince Albert. Over six million people saw the fair, at which exhibitors from all over the world displayed the products of their arts and industry. A substantial profit was made and used to establish museums and a number of scholarships at British universities. In 1895, Rutherford competed for one of these with another New Zealander, J. C. Maclaurin. While Rutherford had studied the magnetization of iron by radio waves, Maclaurin had done work on the purification of gold. As might be expected, gold triumphed in this contest with the baser metal. Maclaurin, however, had meanwhile accepted another position, and Rutherford journeyed to England to study science.

In 1895 the opportunities for research in physics were extremely limited, even in England. There was only one important university laboratory, the Cavendish Laboratory at Cambridge. This had been completed the year of Rutherford's birth, and the first Cavendish professor had been the great James Clerk Maxwell.

Since 1884, the Cavendish had been under the direction of

Sir Joseph John Thomson, a pioneer in electricity. J. J., as he was known to his colleagues, welcomed young Rutherford as a research student at his laboratory, which had recently been established at Cambridge to enable scientists to obtain a degree by doing original research at the Cavendish rather than merely attending lectures.

At Cambridge, Rutherford continued his work on the magnetization of iron by radio waves. Roentgen's discovery of the new mystery waves stimulated Rutherford to do new experiments. With Thomson, he studied the ionization of gases by these X rays. Air is ordinarily an insulator, and its atoms have no charge. But if radiation such as X rays knocks electrons away from some atoms, the atoms become ions. The air is said to be *ionized*. The ions, having electrical charge themselves, move when a charged body is near them, making the air conductive. This had been known before Thomson and Rutherford began their work. However, with his usual experimental brilliance, Rutherford now replaced this qualitative knowledge by more definite quantitative laws. He carefully measured the amount of charge produced when a beam of X rays traversed a gas at reduced pressure.

All of Rutherford's achievements were a result of his ability to quantify his observations. As long as natural phenomena are described in only a qualitative way, many explanations appear equally valid. It requires the more difficultly obtained numerical relationships to distinguish the correct theory from the contending possible explanations.

Roentgen's discovery of the X ray had, of course, created a sensation in the scientific world. Here were rays which could pass through matter that was opaque to ordinary light. With them, the bones in the living hand could be recorded on a photographic plate. If the curiosity of the physicists was not sufficiently aroused, their medical colleagues were sure to knock on the laboratory door and demand that X-ray tubes be set up so that they would be able to look through their patients.

If Roentgen could find X rays by accident, perhaps there

were other types of rays waiting to be discovered. So argued the French physicist Henri Becquerel. When X rays are produced in a glass tube, they fluoresce. There were other substances that fluoresced after they had been illuminated by sunlight. Perhaps they also emitted mystery rays. Becquerel started checking such materials by placing them over a photographic plate that was wrapped in black paper. He tried several fluorescent substances, but they did not affect the plate. In 1896, when he tested crystals of a uranium compound, he was successful—the photographic plate darkened.

Becquerel soon found that his original hunch was wrong. The new rays had nothing to do with fluorescence. Any compound of uranium would darken the plate whether it fluoresced or not, and other fluorescent minerals had no effect on the plate. These rays were emitted without anything being done to the material; they depended only upon its containing the element uranium. He left the uranium salts in a desk drawer and found that they darkened a photographic plate that had been completely sealed. Roentgen's rays were curious; Bequerel's rays shook the very foundations of physics. Their full implications for man still remain to be determined. The darkened photographic plate of Becquerel was the first clue to the power locked in the atom.

Mme. Marie Curie, who named this phenomenon *radioactivity,* and her husband, Pierre, found that some minerals from which uranium was extracted were more active than the uranium itself. Using the new radiation's ability to make air conductive as a guide, they started separating the ores chemically. By 1898, the Curies had found two new elements, one of which they named *radium* and the other *polonium,* after Mme. Curie's native Poland. The minute amount of radium separated from the ore was nine hundred times as strong as an equal weight of uranium.

This element shattered the very bases of the sciences of physics and chemistry. Since the beginning of time, man had attempted to outwit nature and build a machine that would do work without an expenditure of energy. The failure of these attempts had finally led to the establishment of the principle of the conservation of energy. The mysterious radium, however, always maintained itself at a slightly warmer temperature than its surroundings, indicating that it was continually giving off energy that had no apparent source.

For years alchemists had searched for the philosopher's stone to transmute lesser metals into gold, but in the nineteenth century most chemists accepted as true the immutability of the elements. Rutherford was to show clearly how both these fundamental principles were violated by the heaviest elements.

Rutherford completed his studies on the ionization of air by X rays, and then studied ionization by ultraviolet rays (Einstein's photoelectric effect). He then left Cambridge to accept a post as professor at McGill University, in Montreal, Canada, where a new physics laboratory had been established. There, he began the study of radioactivity which he was to continue at Manchester University, England, and then, as Thomson's successor, at the Cavendish Laboratory. The unraveling of the mysteries surrounding Becquerel's rays is a full-length detective story. Here we can touch only upon a few highlights of this adventure.

Rutherford and others had found that the radiation was not all of one kind. In 1899, Rutherford noted that there were at least two distinct types, which he called *alpha* and *beta rays,* after the first two letters of the Greek alphabet. In 1903, he showed that the alpha rays, his special interest, were ions of the gas *helium.* The beta rays were found to be electrons. To this list was added the *gamma ray.* While the alpha and beta rays are now known to consist of streams of particles—helium ions and electrons—gamma rays are very energetic electromagnetic waves. All this radiation was emitted by the radioactive elements according to the laws of probability. During a fixed interval, which varies from element to element, exactly one-half of all the atoms would give off radiation and change into a new material. This is known as the element's *half-life*. During twice that time, the element would be reduced to one-quarter of its original amount.

The rate of decay is independent of the chemical or physical state in which the element finds itself, and of how much of the substance there is. The release of the rays liberates a fantastic amount of energy. Elements also give off energy when they change their chemical state. For example, when coal burns, it releases heat. For a given weight of a radioactive element, however, the heat released by chemical changes is only about one-millionth of that given off during radioactive disintegration. Also, the rate of heat emitted by a chemical change depends on the temperature at which it takes place. At a high temperature, coal burns faster. The release of radioactivity, on the other hand, is independent of the temperature of the material. It cannot be altered by anything we do to it, such as compressing it, heating it, or charging it electrically.

The heat given off in radioactive decay has an important bearing on the age of the earth. Using the principle of the conservation of energy and the laws of cooling, the Scottish mathematician and physicist Lord Kelvin had attacked the notions of the age of the earth held by geologists. His calculations showed that according to these laws, if the earth had formed as a molten ball and cooled since then, it could only be twenty to forty million years old. Similarly, if the sun derives its heat only from chemical or gravitational energy, it can shed its light for only another ten million years.

Rutherford pointed out that the heat released by the radioactive elements contained in the rocks of the earth drastically alters Kelvin's calculations. Once he lectured on this subject, and to his dismay noticed that Lord Kelvin was in the audience. Fortunately Lord Kelvin fell asleep during the talk. Rutherford later wrote that as he came to the important part of his speech:

*"I saw the old bird sit up, open an eye and cock a
baleful glance at me. Then a sudden inspiration came, and
I said Lord Kelvin had limited the age of the earth,* provided no new source was discovered. *That prophetic ut-
terance refers to what we are now considering tonight, radium.*

Thus Rutherford pleased "the old bird" and added an amend-
ment to the law of the conservation of energy.

His lecture was heralded in the press with the headline
"DOOMSDAY POSTPONED." The "doomsday" refers to the
day twenty million years away when, according to Kelvin, the
earth would be too cold for life. Today the relationship between
radioactivity and doomsday is unfortunately less optimistic than
it was at the beginning of the century.

One day, Rutherford was walking on the campus holding a
piece of uranium ore in his hand. He met the professor of geology
and asked him the age of the earth. The professor did not know
for sure, but he thought that the consensus of his colleagues was
that the earth had existed for perhaps a hundred million years.
To this Rutherford replied that he did not know how old the
earth was, but he knew that the piece of rock he was holding
was at least 700 million years old.

He had carefully determined the amount of radium in the
mineral. The radium gives off alpha particles, which remain in
the dense mineral as helium gas. By determining the helium content of the mineral, it is possible to calculate how long it has
been accumulating, assuming that none leaks out. Thus, Rutherford was able to get an estimate of the minimum age of the piece
of rock. Today, more accurate methods are used. The radioactive
elements in a mineral ultimately decay to different types of lead.
By measuring the lead and the amount of the radioactive elements
present, it is possible to determine fairly accurately how long a

piece of rock has existed as a solid mineral. The oldest rocks found show that they were formed several billion years ago.

In this short space we cannot recount all the significant contributions that Rutherford made to the study of radioactivity. Before leaving him, however, we must tell of his greatest discovery.

The physicist Charles G. Darwin, grandson of the famous biologist, recounts as one of the greatest events of his life the time he was present "half an hour after the nucleus was born." This occurred in 1908, before a Sunday-night dinner at Rutherford's house in Manchester. Rutherford had been studying the passage of alpha particles through thin foils of gold. His assistant, a German physicist named Hans Geiger, had been observing the path of these particles as they came through the foil by looking at the flashes of light they produced when they hit a crystal of zinc sulphide. He had been carefully counting the flashes under a microscope and had found that the thin beam was not very spread out by passing through the foil, but that some particles were deviated by a large amount.

Geiger had a young student, Ernest Marsden, working with him, and one day he felt that Marsden was ready to start a research project of his own. When Rutherford was asked to suggest a problem, he told Marsden to investigate the alpha particles that were scattered through a large angle. No one was more surprised than Rutherford when Marsden and Geiger reported a few days later that they could observe that some alpha particles actually turned around and came out of the same side of the foil which they had entered. To quote Rutherford: "It was quite the most incredible event that ever happened to me in my life. It was almost as incredible as if you fired a 15-inch shell at a piece of tissue paper and it came back and hit you."

The fact that it was possible to shoot alpha particles through a piece of foil that would not let ordinary helium through indicated that the atom must have a somewhat open structure; most

of the alpha particles traversed the dense gold with only slight deflections. These deflections could be the result of very many weak collisions between the alpha particle and the atoms of the gold. The alpha particles were incredibly powerful projectiles traveling with one-fifteenth the velocity of light. How could they be turned back in their tracks by the thin foil of gold? It would take an enormous force, which would have to be the result of a single collision.

For a long time Rutherford pondered this riddle of the atomic cannonball that was bounced back by the gold foil. He finally concluded that most of the atom's mass must be concentrated in an extremely small center, or *nucleus,* which carried an electrical charge. Only this way would the forces be adequate to turn back the alpha particle. Since electrical forces obey the same kind of laws as gravity, he made use of Newtonian mechanics to calculate the paths of the particles through the atom. The alpha particle seemed a comet that passed at various distances from a heavy sun. Soon Rutherford decided that the center of the atom must have a positive charge and will thus repel the alpha particle rather than attract it. He predicted the way the particles should be scattered, and set Geiger and Marsden to work recording the distribution of alphas scattered by various foils at different angles. When the results were in, the data exactly fitted Rutherford's theory.

Thus, the idea of the atomic nucleus was born. An unexpected observation led to a new theory. The theory was then tested by careful experimentation, and nature returned a verdict of proven.

From the largest scatterings observed, it was possible to get an idea of the size of the atomic nucleus. Atoms themselves are very small. To fill the distance of one inch, one hundred million gold atoms would have to be placed one next to the other. If one of these atoms is enlarged until it is one mile in diameter, the nucleus of this giant atom would measure only about an inch in diameter. Such is the emptiness of the atom.

The next problem was to show how the positively charged nucleus was combined with negatively charged electrons to produce a neutral atom. This was accomplished two years later, in 1913, by the Danish physicist Niels Bohr. Bohr used a concept of energy that had been put forth by the German physicist Max Planck some years earlier. Planck had said that energy, like matter, exists in particles, or *quanta,* that cannot be further divided. When energy is absorbed or emitted, it is always in whole units, never in parts. A body might emit 3 quanta, or 4, or 5, but never 3.2 quanta. Einstein had used the *photon,* the quantum of light, as the key to his explanation of the photoelectric effect.

Bohr made two assumptions that enabled him to solve the problem. First, he stated that electrons, which revolve in orbits around the nucleus, could have only certain orbits. These were those known as *stationary states;* that is, while the electron was in constant motion, the energy of the atom was assumed to be constant. The orbit had a quantum number, which, of course, was an integer, never a fraction. Secondly, Bohr postulated that an electron did not gradually slide up or down to another level of energy, slowly changing its orbit. Rather, the electron jumped to another level. And the energy absorbed or released would be just one quantum. Once that energy radiated from the atom, if a stable orbit had been reached the energy of the atom was again constant until another electron jump should be made.

Enrico Fermi

CHAPTER 15

Fermi

Einstein predicted by his famous formula $E = mc^2$ that an enormous amount of energy could be released by the loss of a small amount of mass. Rutherford indicated that the energy released by radioactive decay warmed our planet both from within and indirectly by radiation from the sun. Rutherford and others had found that there was no way to alter or control the natural rate of radioactive decay. A radioactive element releases its energy at a fixed rate. It remained for the Italian physicist Enrico Fermi to show how this energy could be controlled by man. On December 2, 1942, Fermi ushered in the atomic age—the beginning of another aspect of the story of physics, which will not be told in this volume.

Enrico Fermi was born in Rome in 1901. In school he disappointed his teachers by his lack of imagination. His compositions were very short, for he insisted on coming straight to the point. He and his brother Giulio, who was one year his senior, were very close friends. When Giulio died at an early age, it was a heavy blow to the young Fermi. He grew more serious, turning away from play to a study of mathematics and physics. His father had few books, and there were no public libraries. Since Fermi could not afford to buy new books, he would hunt through the secondhand stores at Campo dei Fiori, an outdoor market held each Wednesday, in search of volumes on science. One day he picked up a work on physics that fascinated him so much, he did not realize until after he had finished it that it was written not in Italian but in Latin.

Fermi's father had a friend who was an engineer and delighted in giving Enrico simple problems to solve. The lad did so well at this that soon he was solving problems that had stumped the engineer. As a result, Fermi was encouraged to apply to the technical university established in Pisa by Napoleon.

Fermi found that he did not need to study. Instead, he joined the Anti-Neighbors Society, which delighted in precariously balancing pails of water and constructing stink bombs. Each member of the society was required to carry with him at all times a padlock, which he fastened through the buttonholes of unsuspecting friends. Soon the student was teaching his professor theoretical physics and initiating him into Einstein's theory of relativity. In 1922, Fermi obtained his doctor's degree in physics, with a thesis on X rays.

Since Italy was at the time backward in physics, Fermi went off to Germany for two years, to the famous University of Göttingen, to study under Professor Max Born. The chairman of the physics department at the University of Rome, Senator Corbino, was determined to improve the state of physics in Italy, and he brought a number of young men to Rome to revitalize the field. In 1926, he hired Fermi to lead this group, and appointed him a full professor of theoretical physics.

At first Fermi concentrated on theoretical problems—among them, the emission theory of the beta particle. This process was very puzzling, for each beta particle should have been emitted with the same energy, but most seem to have been emitted with less. What happened to this missing energy? Fermi showed that the strange behavior could be explained if one assumed that an already postulated (by Wolfgang Pauli) small, undetectable, neutral particle, which he called the *neutrino,* was emitted at the same time as the beta particle. Fermi's important paper was not appreciated at the time and was even turned down by the English scientific journal *Nature.* Disappointed, he decided to abandon theory for awhile, and concentrate on experimental researches.

Fermi continued his study of neutral particles by turning to the neutron, a neutral particle that has the same mass as the hydrogen atom. The story of the neutron starts in 1930. Two German physicists, Walter Bothe and H. Becker, found that if very energetic alpha particles are used to bombard the metal beryllium, an extremely penetrating type of radiation is produced. At first, it was thought that this radiation consisted of very energetic gamma rays. In 1932, Irène Joliot-Curie, the daughter of the discoverers of radium, together with her husband, Frédéric Joliot, showed that if this penetrating radiation fell on paraffin or other materials containing hydrogen, it produced energetic hydrogen nuclei, known as *protons*. Finally, later that year, Sir James Chadwick, in England, conclusively showed that the penetrating radiation could not be gamma rays, but, rather, consisted of *neutrons*, nuclear particles having no charge and a mass equal to that of the proton. The explanation of the experiment was this: When the alpha particles bombarded the beryllium, they knocked the neutrons loose from the beryllium atoms. These neutrons, in turn, were knocking protons out of the paraffin. Thus, the neutron was discovered.

Fermi's problem was how to use neutrons to bombard elements in order to get nuclear changes. Many atomic transformations had been achieved by bombarding elements with alpha or beta particles given off by radioactive elements. Now it is more usual to use particles that have been accelerated to a high velocity in an "atom-smashing" machine. Sir John Douglas Cockroft and Ernest T. S. Walton in England and Ernest O. Lawrence in the United States succeeded in first artificially accelerating protons with this new machine. The fast protons produced were then used to bombard various elements, giving rise, in the lighter elements, to nuclear transformations.

The atom smashers were able to accelerate the protons because they carried an electrical charge. However, this charge presented a problem. As the particle approached a nucleus, strong

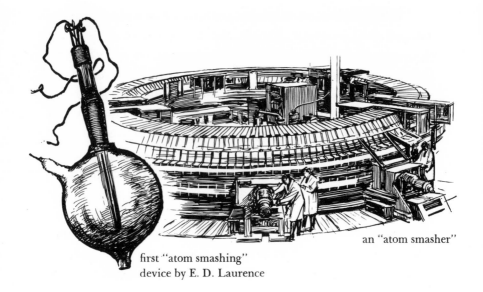

first "atom smashing"
device by E. D. Laurence

an "atom smasher"

electrostatic repulsive forces came into play. These are the same forces that caused Rutherford's gold foil to bounce the alpha particle back in the direction from which it came. Because of electrostatic repulsion, it was impossible to get the bombarding particle close enough to a heavy nucleus to disrupt it. The neutron, on the other hand, was without charge, and so would not be repelled by a nucleus. However, there were no bottles of neutrons available and no machines that could accelerate them. The only way to get neutrons was to allow alpha particles to hit beryllium.

To produce a strong source of neutrons, it was necessary to have radium. Only radium gave off enough alpha particles to construct an intense neutron source from the beryllium. The physics department at Rome was too poor to afford this expensive element. Fortunately, however, the director of the physics laboratory of Rome's Department of Public Health, Professor Giulio Cesare Trabacchi, had a whole gram of radium. This he put at Fermi's disposal. So they mixed *radon,* the radioactive gas given off by the radium, with beryllium to produce neutrons.

To see what materials neutrons affected, the elements were exposed to neutron radiation one by one. Next, it was necessary to remove the material from the source and check its radioactivity with a Geiger counter, which Fermi had built himself. He started irradiation with the lightest element, hydrogen, in the form of its oxide—namely, water. It showed no activity. Next came lithium—again no activity. Beryllium, boron, carbon, and nitrogen also showed no activity. Fermi already knew that oxygen would not respond, so he irradiated fluorine. It is good that Fermi had not given up after the first seven elements, for fluorine was strongly activated. Many of the elements heavier than fluorine were also affected by neutrons. He started to study systematically all the elements he could find. To obtain samples of the rarer ones, his colleague, Emilio Segré, went searching through all the chemical supply houses in Rome.

The activation experiments were exciting to watch. Visitors to the laboratory were surprised to see the professor holding a small sample of an element and running as fast as possible down the corridor. This was because there was a high background of radiation near the neutron source. To detect the much weaker induced activity, the Geiger counter had to be located far away from the source. However, some of the activity produced by the neutrons decayed very rapidly. Therefore, Fermi had to run with the sample down the corridor, racing against the rate of radioactive decay.

When Fermi reached the heaviest element of all, uranium, it became even more strongly radioactive than usual. Some of the uranium was transformed into a radioactive form of another element, but the element was unknown.

He tried to identify the product with one of the elements just below uranium, without success. The evidence seemed to indicate that he had produced a new element beyond uranium, but still Fermi was not absolutely sure. He ended his published report with the prophetic sentence: "It seems, therefore, at present premature to form a definite hypothesis on the chain of disintegrations involved." The full explanation had to await the work of the German chemists Otto Hahn and F. Strassmann, in 1939.

Meanwhile, however, irradiation experiments in Rome continued. To activate various metals, they were shaped into hollow cylinders into which the neutron source was placed. For safety, the assembly, in turn, was put into a lead box in order to confine the penetrating radiation, most of which did not go through the lead.

Fermi then interposed various other materials between the source and a silver foil to see if the amount of radioactivity changed. Lead slightly increased the activity produced. Next, he tried a light material, paraffin, which contains a great deal of hydrogen, and the activity in the silver was greatly increased.

Fermi tried to explain the amplification produced by paraffin. The hydrogen atoms in it might be responsible for the greater efficiency of the neutrons. A hydrogen atom has about the same mass as a neutron, while the lead atom is over two hundred times heavier.

Let us think of the various particles as billiard balls. The hydrogen atoms and neutrons would be very lightweight balls, while the lead balls would, of course, be much heavier. If a light ball collides with another of equal mass, the energy is shared between them, and after the collision, both billiard balls move with approximately equal energy and at less velocity than either had had before.

On the other hand, if the light ball collides with one of the heavy lead ones, the heavy ball is hardly affected, and the light one bounces back with almost its full initial velocity. As the neutron balls keep rolling on the billiard table, they gradually lose their energy as they continue colliding with the hydrogen balls. Yet on a table full of lead balls, they would lose their energy much more slowly.

Perhaps the slow neutrons were more effective in activating

the silver than the fast ones originally given off by the source. If this theory was correct, any material containing hydrogen, such as water, should increase the activity produced by neutrons. To find out, the source and the silver were moved to the largest supply of water available to the physicists. This was provided by Senator Corbino, who had a garden in back of the laboratory whose focal point was a goldfish pond. The goldfish of Senator Corbino became the witnesses of one of the crucial experiments of modern physics. Water, as predicted by Fermi, did increase the activity of silver. Apparently slow-moving neutrons penetrate atomic nuclei more easily.

The experiment of the goldfish pond led to a new series of investigations. All the elements that had been irradiated by fast neutrons now had to be tested again, using neutrons slowed down by hydrogen. During this time, Fermi became more and more disturbed by the political developments in Mussolini's Italy. When he was awarded the Nobel Prize in Stockholm, in December 1938, he used the occasion to move permanently to the United States. On January 2, 1939, the Fermis landed in New York, and Enrico exclaimed that they had founded the American branch of the Fermi family.

Two weeks after the Fermis arrived in New York, they had a visitor with important news—Niels Bohr, the architect of the atom, arrived from Denmark. There, a refugee scientist from Hitler's Germany, Lise Meitner, had reported to Bohr on her work with Professors Hahn and Strassmann. They had reexamined the effect of neutrons on uranium, and had found radioactive barium among the elements produced. Barium is a much lighter element than uranium, with about one-half its mass.

So far, naturally radioactive elements had been known to give off alpha, beta, and gamma rays. In addition to these, artificially activated nuclei also emitted protons and neutrons. Now the German chemists showed that the heavy uranium nucleus apparently responded to neutron activation in a different way.

Instead of giving off a lightweight particle, it literally split in two. It was like a water drop that, having grown too heavy for its surface tension to hold it together, divides into two roughly equal drops. Lise Meitner called this process *fission.*

Her news created a great deal of excitement among Fermi and the other physicists working at Columbia University. It had been known that when protons and neutrons unite to form atomic nuclei, some of their mass is lost when the particles around are bound together, or *packed.* This loss per particle, or *packing factor,* corresponds to the energy that is emitted when the binding takes place. Elements vary in the packing factor. Barium and other elements of intermediate mass have a higher packing factor than the others which are lighter or heavier. Thus, the sum of the masses into which the uranium splits is less than the mass of the uranium. The lost mass is given off as energy in accordance with Einstein's formula. Similarly, if nuclei of elements light in mass are combined to form a nucleus of an element of intermediate mass, the packing factor is again increased, and energy is liberated. This is known as *fusion,* and is responsible for the heat generated by the sun.

Uranium fission, therefore, gives rise to a large release of energy, over twenty times as much energy as is liberated by ordinary alpha-particle bombardment. As a result of the energy released, the fragments of uranium should move apart with very great velocities.

The energy released by uranium fission, however, would be useful only if it could be controlled. It was here that another factor entered. Not only are the elements of intermediate mass more tightly bound than others, but the elements formed by the fission process contain a smaller total number of neutrons than is in the original uranium. It appeared likely, therefore, that neutrons would be emitted as a result of fission. It might then be possible to utilize a fraction of the neutrons produced to initiate a new fission process, and so on. The importance of this possibility was immediately grasped by Fermi.

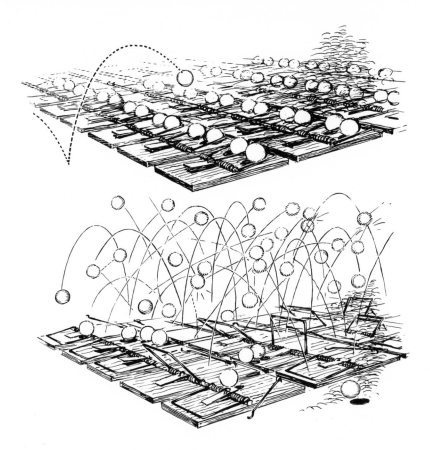

The process by which the neutrons released in fission can split one or more new uranium nuclei and thus make the reaction self-sustaining is known as a *chain reaction.* To visualize a chain reaction, let us imagine a room full of mousetraps. Instead of baiting them with cheese, we place two ping-pong balls on the cocked spring of each trap. All is quiet. Now another ping-pong ball is dropped on the floor among the loaded traps. If the traps are placed close enough together, the ball, perhaps after bouncing a few times, will set off a trap. This now projects its two balls into the air, setting off one or two new traps. These pop more traps, and soon there are ping-pong balls bouncing all over the floor, until most of the traps have released their balls. In this chain reaction, one single ball dropped on the floor eventually sets off hundreds of traps.

If the traps are too far apart, or if there are not enough of them, the balls that have been released will come to rest before many traps have been set off. To obtain a chain reaction, it is necessary to have the traps packed tightly together and to have enough of them, so that most of the balls do not bounce outside the area covered by the traps. Of course, the more balls each trap carries, the easier it will be to start a chain reaction.

To be able to predict what will happen in the fission process, it is necessary to know the number of neutrons given off at the fission of each uranium nucleus, the way the neutrons behave after they are emitted, and the probability that a given neutron will initiate another fission. With that information, it would then be possible to construct the optimum array of uranium to produce a chain reaction.

At first sight it might appear that a chain reaction is something that cannot be controlled. Either it does not begin or it continuously multiplies until all the uranium is used up in one big explosion.

However, the chain reaction can be controlled. At first, the rate of fission is allowed to build up. If there were no interference, it would continue to increase. After a desired level has been reached, however, some material is introduced that will use up some of the neutrons, and so stop or reduce the chain reaction. The energy level will now drop, and soon the control material must be removed in order to let the reaction build up once more.

First at Columbia University and then at the University of Chicago, Fermi tried to establish a controlled chain reaction. The problem was complicated by the fact that there are two types of uranium atoms—the *isotopes* U 235 and U 238. Isotopes are chemically identical elements with different atomic weights. Only U 235, which makes up less than one per cent of natural uranium, readily undergoes fission; moreover, U 238 strongly absorbs the neutrons given off by U 235. One way to avoid this difficulty is to separate the two isotopes and eliminate the U 238. This extremely difficult separation was accomplished in large plants built for this purpose. Meanwhile, however, Fermi proceeded on a different plan.

Through his work in Rome, he had shown that neutrons of varying energies have different effects on the elements. He found that slow neutrons were more likely to cause fission in U 235 than fast ones. Also, the faster neutrons were more readily absorbed by U 238. Then the fission process could be increased if the neutrons produced by uranium fission were slowed down before they bombarded more uranium. Once they were slowed down, they could initiate additional fission with little chance of being absorbed by U 238. It is important that during the slowing-down process, the neutrons are not absorbed; ordinary hydrogen absorbs too many neutrons to be efficient in this process.

The slowing-down medium, or *moderator,* chosen was extremely pure carbon, in the form of graphite, throughout which pieces of uranium were distributed. The fabrication and assembling of the apparatus made the physicists look more like coal miners than scientists. Gradually, the pile of graphite and uranium took shape and then, on December 2, 1942, in a squash court under the west stands of the football field of the University of Chicago, Fermi slowly had the control rods withdrawn, initiating the first self-sustaining chain reaction. Thus, the former member of the padlock-carrying Anti-Neighbors Society had unlocked the energy of the nucleus. The word passed to Washington in the following code:

CHICAGO: "The Italian Navigator has reached the New World."

WASHINGTON: "And how did he find the natives?"

CHICAGO: "Very friendly."

There are many romantic stories of pirate gold found on treasure islands and of ancient cities rediscovered in the jungle. These treasures, however, are insignificant compared to the secrets that have been found by the application of the human mind to the wonders of nature. An Archimedes in his bathtub, a Galileo watching the swing of a lamp, a Fermi putting his neutron source into the goldfish pond made more important discoveries than Marco Polo or Christopher Columbus. The discovery of the New World and all the gold of the Incas had less effect on man than the discovery of the atomic nucleus and the operation of the chain-reacting pile. This is the romance of physics. Man looks at nature, thinks and experiments, and, by so doing, transforms the world.

c.3rd Century B.C.	Ctesibius develops first air pump
c.287 B.C.	Archimedes, mathematician and inventor, born (died 212 B.C.)
1590 A.D.	Invention of the telescope in the Netherlands by Hans Lippershey
1593	Galileo Galilei (1564–1642) invents the thermometer
1600	William Gilbert (1546–1603) publishes *On Magnetism*
1610	Galileo publishes the *Starry Messenger*, a pamphlet listing his early astronomical observations
1632	Publication of Galileo's *Dialogue on the Two Chief World Systems*, which advocated the theory that the planets revolve around the sun
1638	Galileo's *Discourses Concerning Two New Sciences* published, reporting his discoveries and inventions in mechanics
1642	Isaac Newton born (died 1727)
1643	Evangelista Torricelli (1608–1647) invents the barometer
1646	Blaise Pascal (1623–1662) tests the effects of air pressure at varying altitudes on the barometer
1650	Otto von Guericke (1602–1686) invents the air pump
1665	Isaac Newton (1642–1727) develops the theory of gravitation
1666	Newton develops the theory of light and colors after experimenting with prisms
1687	Newton's *Principia*, setting forth his views on gravitation, is published
1704	*Optics*, a summary of all his work in the field, published by Newton
1709	Gabriel Daniel Fahrenheit (1686–1736) invents

	his thermometer and a scale to measure temperature
1714	Fahrenheit uses mercury in a thermometer for the first time
1742	Anders Celsius (1701–1744) introduces his system (centigrade) of temperature measurement
1746	Peter van Musschenbroek (1692–1761) develops the first Leyden jar
1752	Benjamin Franklin (1706–1790) proves that lightning and the Leyden jar possess the same kind of electricity
1791	Luigi Galvani (1737–1798) concludes his experiments on animal electricity
1796	Alessandro Volta (1745–1827) constructs the first voltaic pile
1800	William Herschel (1738–1822) discovers infrared light
1801	Ultraviolet light discovered
1803	John Dalton (1766–1844) begins his formulation of the atomic theory of gases
	Thomas Young (1773–1829) proposes a wave theory of light
1811	Amadeo Avogadro (1776–1856) develops the molecular theory of gases
1820	Hans Christian Oersted (1777–1851) discovers the relationship between electricity and magnetism
	André Marie Ampère (1775–1836) develops the theory that electromagnetism is an effect of electric current
1821	Michael Faraday (1791–1867) builds the first magnetoelectric motor
1823	William Sturgeon (1783–1850) invents the electromagnet
1827	Robert Brown (1773–1858) observes *Brownian motion* of particles in liquid

1831   Joseph Henry (1797–1878) builds the first tele-
            graph
            Faraday proposes that electricity can be pro-
            duced by magnetism
1833   Faraday delivers his paper on the "identity of
            electricities" to the Royal Society
1835   Samuel F. B. Morse (1791–1872) builds the first
            model of his telegraph
1838   Faraday reports on his studies of transmission of
            electricity through a vacuum tube
1843   James Joule (1818–1889) shows how the me-
            chanical equivalent of heat can be deter-
            mined in *On the Heat Evolved during the Elec-
            trolysis of Water*
1864   James Clark Maxwell (1831–1879) develops the
            theory that all electromagnetic energy trav-
            els in waves at the speed of light
1876   Alexander Graham Bell (1847–1922) patents the
            telephone
1879   William Crookes (1832–1919) observes the pas-
            sage of negative particles of electricity (elec-
            trons) through a vacuum tube
            Thomas Alva Edison (1847–1931) succeeds in
            making practical incandescent lamps
1887   Heinrich R. Hertz (1857–1894) demonstrates
            the existence of electromagnetic waves
1895   Wilhelm Roentgen (1845–1923) discovers X rays
1896   Antoine Henri Becquerel (1852–1908) observes
            the radioactivity of uranium for the first
            time
1897   Guglielmo Marconi (1874–1937) patents the
            first wireless telegraph
            J. J. Thomson (1856–1940) proves the existence
            of the electron and determines its prop-
            erties
1898   Marie Curie (1867–1934) and her husband
            Pierre (1859–1906) discover radium

1899	Ernest Rutherford (1871–1937) finds and names alpha and beta rays
1905	Albert Einstein (1879–1955) publishes a series of scientific papers explaining brownian motion and the photoelectric effect and proposing the Special Theory of Relativity
1908	Rutherford develops the theoretical concept of the atomic nucleus
1913	Niels Bohr (1885–1962) proposes the "energy level" concept of electrons in orbit about the atomic nucleus
1926	Enrico Fermi (1901–1954) discovers the neutrino
1927	Albert A. Michelson (1852–1931) succeeds in obtaining almost the exact figure of the speed of light
1933	Irène Joliot-Curie (1897–1956) and her husband Frèdèric (1900–1958) identify neutron radiation
1942	First successful atomic chain reaction at the University of Chicago under Fermi's direction

alpha rays, radiation consisting of helium nuclei, positively charged particles each with two protons and two electrons.

alternating current, one that periodically reverses the direction of its current flow.

amplitude, the maximum displacement of a wave or oscillation from its equilibrium position.

Ångstrom unit (Å), a length of 10^{-10} meters used as a unit to express wavelengths of light. Thus, visible light has a range of wavelengths from 4000Å to 7000Å.

anode, see *vacuum tube.*

atom, the smallest particle of an element that retains the physical and chemical properties of that element.

barometer, an instrument used to measure atmospheric pressure.

battery, a collection of two or more chemical cells used to supply electrical energy.

beta rays, radiation consisting of electrons or positrons emitted from the nucleus of an atom.

Brownian motion, a random movement of small particles suspended in a fluid.

calculus, a type of mathematics that deals with processes involving the taking of a limit and the rate of change of a function. It can be applied to problems involving such continually varying quantities as velocity, acceleration, and rate of chemical reaction.

capillary action, movement upward in a container by a liquid whose adhesive force between it and its container is greater than the liquid's own surface tension, or a movement downward when the surface tension of the liquid is the greater.

capillary tube, a tube, usually of glass, of small diameter, in which liquids, due to capillary action, either rise or are depressed. For example, water rises in such a tube, mercury is depressed.

cathode, see *vacuum tube.*

center of gravity, the point of a body at which all the weight seems to be concentrated; at that point the body can be balanced and supported by only one force.

centrigrade, a scale for the measurement of temperature at which the melting point of ice is 0° and the boiling point of water is 100°. To change a centrigrade reading to its Fahrenheit equivalent, multiply by ⅘ and add 32.

centrifugal force, the force a revolving body exerts as a reaction to the centripetal force. It is in opposition to and equal in magnitude to the centripetal force.

centripetal force, the force needed to keep a body moving in a circle; it pulls the body toward the center of the circle around which it revolves.

chain reaction, one that is self-sustaining, because the reaction produces the agent that started the reaction. Thus, in a nuclear chain reaction a neutron causes a nucleus to disintegrate and release other neutrons that can, in turn, cause additional nuclei to disintegrate.

cancave lens, one that is thinner near the center than at its edges; it causes light rays to diverge.

convex lens, one that is thicker near the center than at the edges; it causes light rays to converge.

Coulomb's law, the law of attraction or repulsion beween point electric charges which states that the force of repulsion, *F,* is proportional to the product of the magnitude of two changes (q_1 and q_2) and is inversely proportional to the square of the distance (r) separating the two charges; $F = K \dfrac{q_1 \cdot q_2}{r^2}$ where K is a constant.

cycloid curve, a curve generated by a fixed point on the circumference of a circle that rolls without slipping along a straight line.

direct current, a current that flows only in one direction.

electric charge, the property of certain particles and bodies that results in forces of attraction or repulsion. Charge is either negative or positive, and like charges repel each other while unlike charges attract each other. A body is said to be charged, generally, when it has gained or lost electrons.

electric current, a flow of charged units of electricity; in metals it is generally a flow of electrons.

electric motor, a device that converts electrical energy into mechanical energy.

electricity, the phenomenon associated with charges, usually in the form of electrons, or protons or ions. A form of energy associated with the repulsion and attraction of charges.

electrochemistry, the science concerned with the chemical changes that take place when an electric current is passed into certain conducting solutions, or with the conversion of electrical energy into chemical energy and the reverse.

electrode, in a voltaic cell or other electrochemical apparatus, one of two strips of dissimilar metal, which receive opposite electric charges; the conductor that allows current to pass into a liquid or a gas in cells or certain types of vacuum tubes.

electrolyte, a solution that conducts an electric current.

electromagnet, usually it is a coil of wire wound spirally in a number of layers around a soft iron core. The wire is connected to a source of electricity and when the current is turned on the electromagnet behaves like a strong magnet.

electron, a particle possessing the smallest unit of negative electric charge; 1.6×10^{-19} coulomb; in an atom the particle is in constant motion about the nucleus. It has a mass of 9.11×10^{-31} kg.

electroscope, an instrument used to detect the existence of an electric charge and generally consisting of two light vanes of metallic leaves that can repel each other.

emf (Electromotive Force), the electrical difference in potential expressed in volts generated by a device in which chemical, mechanical, or some other form of energy is changed into electrical energy.

energy, the ability to do work, to cause matter to change.

exciter, a device used with an alternating-current generator or a larger d.c. generator, which supplies it with a source of direct current to activate its field magnets.

Fahrenheit, a scale for the measurement of temperature at which the melting point of ice is $32°$ and the boiling point of water is $212°$. To change a Fahrenheit reading to a centigrade one, subtract 32 from the Fahrenheit reading and multiply by ⅝.

fission, the process in which a heavy atomic nucleus is split into two nearly equal parts, releasing a relatively large amount of energy.

force, push or pull; the agent that changes the motion of a body or produces a strain in a body.

frequency, the number of complete vibrations per second of a vibrating or periodic source; the number of complete waves passing a point each second.

fusion, the process by which light elements are combined to form the nucleus of a heavier element, thus increasing the packing fraction and liberating energy; generally, the conversion of hydrogen to helium.

galvanometer, an instrument that can measure both the direction and intensity of small currents.

gamma rays, electromagnetic radiation of extremely short wavelengths generally associated with reactions involving the nucleus or nuclear particles.

generator, a device that produces electrical energy from some other form of energy.

geometry, the branch of mathematics devoted to the study of figures in space.

gravitation, the force of attraction between two bodies due to the mass of each body. Every particle of matter in the universe attracts every other particle. The strength of the force of gravitation between two bodies depends on the amount of matter of which they are each composed and inversely on the square of the distance between them. The earth's gravitational pull on an object is called its *weight.*

half-life, the time during which exactly one-half of a radioactive element's atoms would give off radiation and change into a new material.

heat, a form of energy; the energy in transit between two bodies, which depends solely on the temperature difference between the bodies. When heat is absorbed by a body it generally increases the kinetic energy of its molecules.

hydraulic machine, one that transmits force by means of fluids.

hydrostatic balance, the name given by Galileo to a type of balance developed by him that weighs objects before and during immersion in water in order to determine their specific gravity.

hyperbola, one of the curves that is a conic section obtained by a plane cutting both surfaces of a conical surface formed by two cones having the same axis and the vertex of one touching the other.

inertia, the tendency of a body in motion to remain in motion or of a body at rest to remain at rest; the mass of a body is a measure of its inertia.

infrared, invisible light waves of wavelength slightly longer than the longest visible red rays.

interference, the interaction or superposition of two waves that meet one another; generally involving waves of the same or nearly the same frequency. If they meet in phase, crest meeting crest, they add constructively. If they meet out of phase, crest meeting trough, they counteract each other and produce destructive interference.

ion, an atom or group of atoms that has become electrically charged.

isotope, chemically identical elements with different atomic masses.

lever, one of the simple machines. The lever is a rigid body free to rotate around an axis, or fulcrum. Generally, one force, the *effort,* is applied to it to overcome a second force, the *resistance.* There are three classes of levers. In the first, the resistance and the effort are on opposite sides of the fulcrum; in the second, both resistance and effort are on the same side of the fulcrum, the resistance being between effort and fulcrum; the third class of lever is like the second, except that the effort is between the fulcrum and the resistance.

Leyden jar, a glass jar coated inside and out with tinfoil or other metal, forming a capacitor. A metal rod with a chain attached to it passes through an insulated stopper so that the chain can come into contact with the inner foil. It can store electrical charge and is discharged when the two coatings, each carrying a different charge, are connected to one another.

magnet, an object that attracts materials such as iron, nickel, and cobalt. Its structure is such that there is a significant alignment of the magnetic fields of its atoms and molecules.

magnetism, the study of the magnetic force of attraction or repulsion.

manometer, an instrument used to measure gas pressure, usually a U tube with a small amount of mercury in the bottom of the U.

mass defect, the difference between the actual atomic mass and the mass number of a nucleus. The mass number is the number of neutrons and protons in a nucleus. This difference is related to the *binding energy*, which holds the nucleus together, and is the energy required to separate it into its constituent elements.

matter, anything that has mass or inertia.

mechanics, the study of states of rest and of motion of bodies and of the forces that act upon them.

mechanical advantage, in a machine, the ratio of the load or resistance moved to the effort applied.

molecule, the smallest particle of a substance that has the chemical and physical properties of that substance and can exist free; generally, it is composed of two or more atoms.

nucleus, the positively charged, central portion of an atom in which most of its mass is concentrated.

neutrino, a small atomic particle of neutral charge and no rest mass.

neutron, an atomic particle of neutral charge with approximately the same mass as a proton.

packing fraction, the ratio between the mass defect of a nucleus and its mass number. It is a measure of the apparent loss of mass per particle in the nucleus and is thus related to the binding energy that keeps the nucleus together.

parabola, a curve that is a conic section, which is obtained by cutting a plane that does not contain a vertex and is parallel to one element of the cone.

paraboloid of revolution, a figure made by rotating a parabola about its long axis.

pendulum, a small, dense body suspended by a lightweight thread from a point so that it is free to swing back and forth.

period, for a periodic function or wave, the time it takes to complete one vibration or for one wavelength to pass a given point.

phase, when applied to periodic functions, it is that part of a period through which the periodic function has passed from some arbitrary starting point. Thus two waves are in phase if they are in step, so that both crest at the same time and trough at the same time. Two waves are out of phase if one crests at some fraction of a period before or after the other.

photoelectric effect, the liberation of electrons from a body as a result of irradiation by light.

photon, the basic unit of energy of electromagnetic waves; the quantum of electromagnetic waves; the energy of a photon is given by Planck's equation $E = hf$, where h is Planck's constant and f is the frequency of the wave.

physics, the study of matter and of the energies that cause it to change. The major topics of it are divided into mechanics, heat, optics, electrical and magnetic energy, atomic physics, and nuclear physics.

Planck's constant, h, 6.624×10^{-34} joule-sec, the constant of proportionality between the energy of a photon and its frequency.

proton, positively charged unit of electricity; a hydrogen nucleus.

pulley, one of the simple machines; it reverses the direction of the applied force.

quantum, the basic unit of energy. When a physical quantity cannot take on a continuous set of values and is restricted to a discrete set of values, it is said to be quantized. The discrete values are always multiples of a basic unit, or quantum.

radiant energy, a form of energy traveling in wave motion from one body to another by the means of electromagnetic radiations; light, heat, and electricity are forms of radiant energy.

radioactivity, the spontaneous emission of energy or particles as a result of the disintegration of the nucleus of an atom.

reflection, when a light ray strikes a surface, if it rebounds and again travels at another angle through the medium from which it has come, it is said to be reflected.

refraction, the change of direction of a light ray or other radiation as it travels at an oblique angle from one medium through another. Refraction occurs when the radiation's speed changes as it enters the second medium.

simple machine, a piece of equipment used to change either the magnitude or the direction of a force; there are six such machines: the pulley, wheel and axle, lever, inclined plane, wedge, and screw.

solar spectrum, the range of wavelengths emitted by the sun and made visible by passing this radiation through a prism or a diffraction grating. The prism disperses the wavelengths into a continuous array of colors from red, the longest visible wavelength, through orange, yellow, green, blue, indigo and violet. With special prisms and with gratings, the invisible infrared and ultraviolet radiations of the sun can also be recorded.

solenoid, a coil of wire that can be connected to a source of electricity so that, when current flows through it, its magnetic field resembles that of a bar magnet.

surface tension, the molecular force at the surface of a fluid that is elastic and tends to make the surface act like a stretched membrane.

thermometer, an instrument used to measure temperature.

ultraviolet, invisible light waves of shorter wavelength than the shortest visible violet rays, ranging from approximately 4000Å to 400Å.

vacuum tube, an enclosure, usually metal or glass, from which most of the air has been pumped, creating a vacuum through which a flow of electrons takes place. The *diode* has a filament, or cathode, connected to a source of electricity, and an anode, a positively charged metallic element. In the *triode,* a grid, a mesh of fine wire, is placed between the positively and negatively charged elements. Other types of vacuum tubes include tetrodes, pentodes, beam-power tubes, as well as a large variety of special tubes.

voltaic cell, a device that changes chemical energy into electrical energy, usually consisting of two electrodes of dissimilar metals in a solution, the *electrolyte,* which acts upon one or both of the electrodes to produce an emf.

volume, the amount of space a body occupies.

wave, a disturbance that travels through space or a medium; a quantity varying with time and position.

wavelength, the horizontal distance between two high crests of a wave, or between any two corresponding points in the same phase in the wave.

wheel and axle, one of the simple machines consisting of a wheel to which a cylinder or axle of smaller radius is rigidly attached. The theoretical mechanical advantage of this device is the ratio of the radius of the wheel to that of the axle.

work, that which is done when a force moves an object a given distance.

X rays, electromagnetic radiation of extremely short wavelength.

Andrade, E. N. da C. *Rutherford and the Nature of the Atom.* Garden City, N.Y.: Doubleday Anchor Books, 1964.

_____. *Sir Isaac Newton.* Garden City, N.Y.: Doubleday Anchor Books, 1954.

Armitage, Angus. *The World of Copernicus.* New York: New American Library Mentor Books, 1951.

Asimov, Isaac. *Inside the Atom.* New York: Abelard-Schuman, 1956.

Barnett, Lincoln. *The Universe and Dr. Einstein.* New York: New American Library Mentor Books, 1952.

Beiser, Arthur. *The World of Physics.* New York: McGraw-Hill, 1960.

Bitter, Francis. *Magnets: The Education of a Physicist.* Garden City, N.Y.: Doubleday Anchor Books, 1959.

Canby, Courtlandt (ed.). *The New Illustrated Library of Science and Invention.* 12 vols. New York: Hawthorn, 1963.

Cohen, I. Bernard. *The Birth of a New Physics.* Garden City, N.Y.: Doubleday Anchor Books, 1960.

_____. *Science, Servant of Man.* Boston: Little, Brown, 1948.

Coleman, James A. *Relativity for the Layman.* New York: New American Library Mentor Books, 1958.

Conant, James Bryant (ed.). *Harvard Case Histories in Experimental Science.* 2 vols. Cambridge, Mass.: Harvard University Press, 1957.

_____. *Modern Science and Modern Man.* Garden City, N.Y.: Doubleday Anchor Books, 1959.

_____. *On Understanding Science.* New York: New American Library Mentor Books, 1951.

Curie, Eve. *Madame Curie.* Garden City, N.Y.: Doubleday, 1949.

d'Abro, A. *The Rise of the New Physics.* 2 vols. New York: Dover Publications, 1953.

Dampier, William Cecil. *A Shorter History of Science.* Cleveland, Ohio: World Publishing Co. Meridan Books, 1957.

Dibner, Bern. *Alessandro Volto and the Electric Battery.* New York: Franklin Watts, 1964.

Eddington, Arthur. *New Pathways in Science.* Ann Arbor, Mich.: University of Michigan Press, 1959.

Fermi, Laura. *Atoms in the Family: My Life with Enrico Fermi.* Chicago: University of Chicago Press, 1954.

Fermi, Laura, and Bernadini, Gilberto. *Galileo and the Scientific Revolution.* New York: Basic Books, 1961.

Fortune, Editors of. *Great American Scientists.* Englewood Cliffs, N.J.: Prentice-Hall, 1961.

Gamow, George. *Biography of Physics.* New York: Harper Torchbooks, 1961.

————. *One, Two, Three . . . Infinity.* New York: Viking Press Compass Books, 1961 (rev. ed.).

————. *Mr. Tompkins Explores the Atom.* New York: Cambridge University Press, 1945.

Gardner, Martin. *Relativity for the Million.* New York: Macmillan, 1962.

Ginzburg, Benjamin. *The Adventure of Science.* New York: Simon & Schuster, 1930.

Heathcote, N. Y. de V. *Nobel Prize Winners in Physics.* New York: Abelard-Schuman, 1953.

Hecht, Selig. *Explaining the Atom.* New York: Viking Press Compass Books, 1954 (revised and enlarged by Eugene Rabinowitch).

Hogben, Lancelot. *Science for the Citizen.* New York: Norton, 1957.

Hope, Richard. *Aristotle's Physics.* Lincoln, Neb.: University of Nebraska Press Bison Books, 1961.

Hoyle, Fred. *Frontiers of Astronomy.* New York: New American Library Mentor Books, 1955.

Hughes, Donald J. *The Neutron Story.* Garden City, N.Y.: Doubleday Anchor Books, 1959.

Jaffe, Bernard. *Michelson and the Speed of Light.* Garden City, N.Y.: Doubleday Anchor Books, 1960.

Jeans, James. *The Universe Around Us.* New York: Cambridge University Press, 1960.

Koestler, Arthur. *A History of Man's Changing Vision of the Universe.* New York: Grosset & Dunlap, 1963.

Levinger, Elma E. *Galileo: First Observer of Marvelous Things.* New York: Messner, 1954.

MacDonald, D. K. C. *Faraday, Maxwell, and Kelvin.* Garden City, N.Y.: Doubleday Anchor Books, 1964.

Magie, W. F. *A Source Book in Physics.* New York: McGraw-Hill, 1935;

also Cambridge, Mass.: Harvard University Press, 1963.

Marcus, Rebecca B. *Antoine Lavoisier and the Revolution in Chemistry.* New York: Franklin Watts, 1965.

Michelmore, Peter. *Einstein—Profile of the Man.* New York: Dodd, Mead, 1962.

Partington, J. R. *A Short History of Chemistry.* New York: Macmillan, 1951.

Pear, Catherine Owens. *Albert Einstein, A Biography for Young People.* New York: Holt, Rinehart & Winston, 1949.

Reichen, Charles, Albert. *A History of Physics.* New York: Hawthorn, 1963.

Reichenbach, Hans. *From Copernicus to Einstein.* New York: Philosophical Library Wisdom Library Paperbacks, 1942.

Reidman, Sarah R. *Trailblazer of American Science: The Life of Joseph Henry.* New York: Rand McNally, 1961.

Sarton, George. *A History of Science.* Vol. 1: *Ancient Science Through the Golden Age of Greece;* Vol. 2: *A History of Hellenistic Science and Culture in the Last Three Centuries.* Cambridge, Mass.: Harvard University Press, 1959.

Semat, Henry. *Physics in the Modern World.* New York: Holt, Rinehart & Winston, 1959.

Semat, Henry, and White, Harvey E. *Atomic Age Physics.* New York: Holt, Rinehart & Winston, 1959.

Shamos, Morris H. (ed.). *Great Experiments in Physics.* New York: Holt, Rinehart & Winston, 1959.

Skilling, Hugh H. *Exploring Electricity: Man's Unfinished Quest.* New York: Ronald Press, 1948.

Sootin, Harry. *Michael Faraday: From Errand Boy to Master Physicist.* New York: Messner, 1954.

Taylor, F. Sherwood. *A Short History of Science and Scientific Thought.* New York: Norton, 1949.

Thiel, Rudolf. *And There Was Light.* New York: New American Library Mentor Books, 1960.

True, Webster P. (ed.). *Smithsonian Treasury of Science.* 3 vols. New York: Simon & Schuster, 1960.

White, Harvey E. *Physics: An Exact Science.* Princeton, N.J.: Van Nostrand, 1959.

INDEX

A. C.; *see* alternating current
Air, volume of, 78
Air pressure, 73, 75–76, 77
    von Guericke's theories of,
        67–69
Air pump, 45, 118, 119
    parts of, 65, 66, 69
    von Guericke's 65–66
Air thermometer, 93
Alcohol thermometer, 97
Alexandria, Egypt, 14, 22, 63
    schoolmen of, 14, 15, 19, 20
Alpha particle, 199–202, 207, 208
Alpha ray, 197, 211
Alternating current, 142
A. M.; *see* amplitude modulation
Ampére, André Marie, 127–128
Amplitude modulation, 172, 174
Animal electricity, Galvani's
    theory of, 111–113, 114
Anode, 119, 173
Archimedes, 11, 13–27, 32, 38–39,
    216
    Great Demonstration of, 26–
        27
    inventions of, 22–26
    Laws of Flotation of, 17–19,
        79
    Law of the Lever of, 19
    Principle of, 18–19
    solution of, to problem of
        King's crown, 16, 32, 39
Aristotle, 89–90
    Galileo's corrections of scien-
        tific errors of, 44–47
    theories of, on falling bodies,
        34–36, 45
Atmospheric electricity, 112
Atmospheric pressure, 93, 97

Atom, 80–81, 182, 195
    composition of, 117
    energy of, 179, 202–203
    size of, determined by Ein-
        stein, 181
Atomic nuclei, 211–212
Atomic theory, 81; *see also* gases,
    Dalton's theory of
Atom-smashing machines, 189,
    207
"Automatic telegraph repeater,"
    139–140
Avogadro, Amedeo, 81

Barium, 211, 212
Barometer, 72–76, 93–94
    invention of, 69
Becker, H., 207
Becquerel, Henri, 196, 197
Bell, Alexander Graham
    birth of, 137
    invention of telephone by,
        137–138
Beryllium, 207, 208
Beta particle, 207
    Fermi's emission theory of
        the, 206
Beta ray, 197, 211
Binomial theorem, of algebra, 55
Bohr, Niels, 202, 211
Boiling point, of water, 97, 150
Born, Max, 206
Bothe, Walter, 207
Boyle, Robert, 61, 76
Boyle's Law, 78, 83
Braun, Karl Ferdinand
    Nobel Prize awarded to, 172
Brown, Robert, 181–183
Brownian motion, 181–182